FOR ORGANS, PIANOS & ELECTRONIC KEYBOARDS

Exclusive Distributors:
MUSIC SALES LIMITED
8/9 Frith Street,
London W1V 5TZ, England.
MUSIC SALES PTY LIMITED
120 Rothschild Avenue, Rosebery,
NSW 2018, Australia.

Order No. HLE90000220
ISBN 0-7119-6429-7

LOVE SONGS

Cover design by Pearce Marchbank, Studio Twenty, London
Printed in the USA

HAL LEONARD EUROPE

And I Love Her

Registration 8
Rhythm: Rock or Jazz Rock

Words and Music by John Lennon
and Paul McCartney

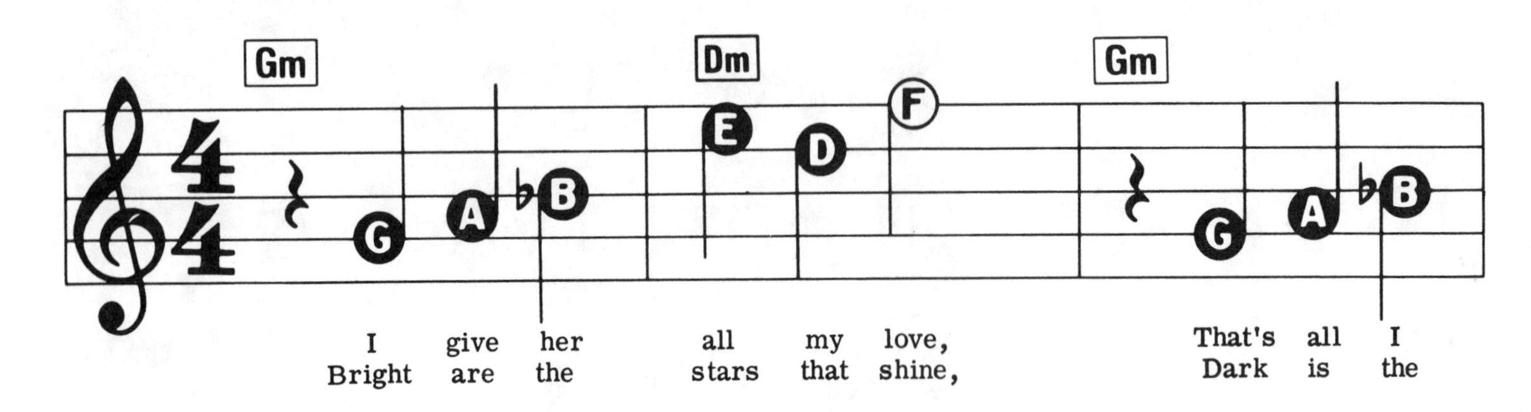

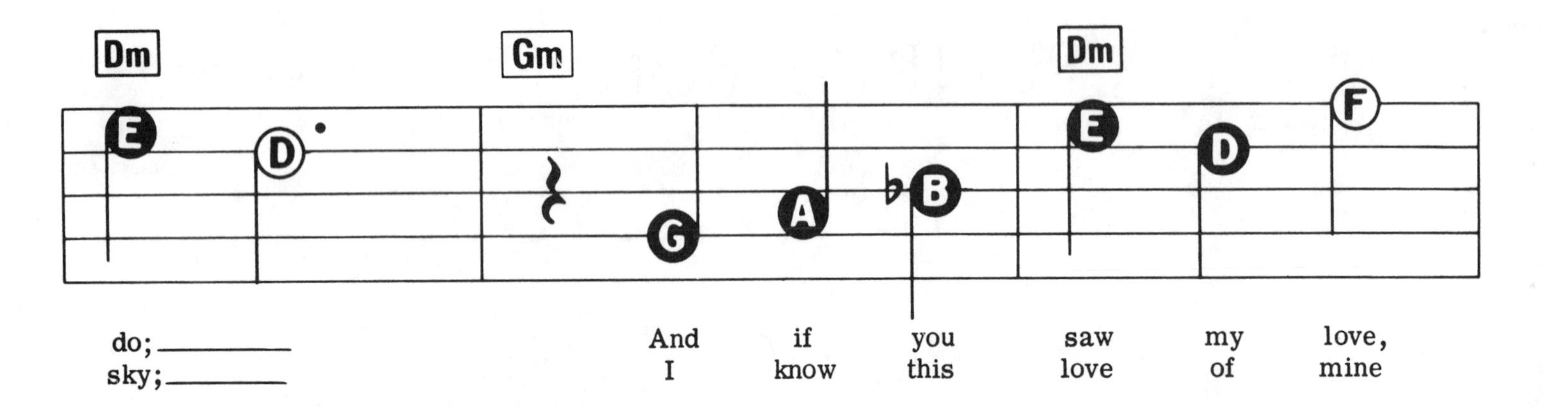

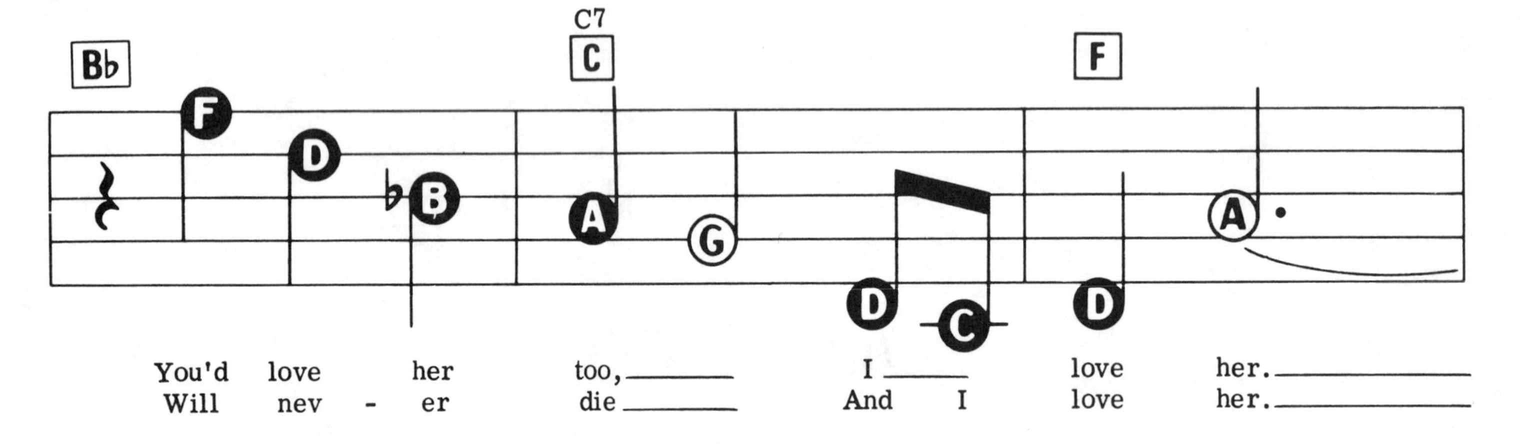

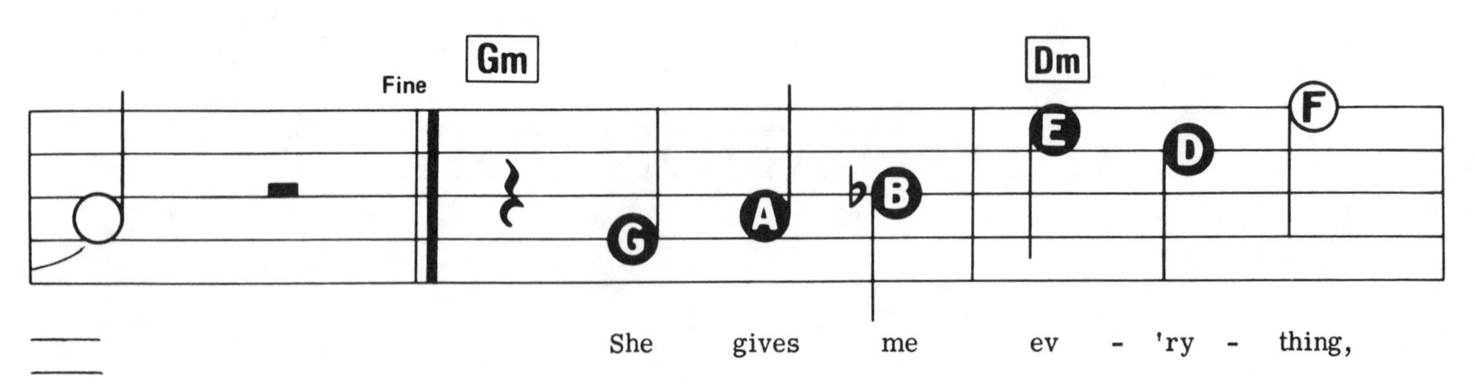

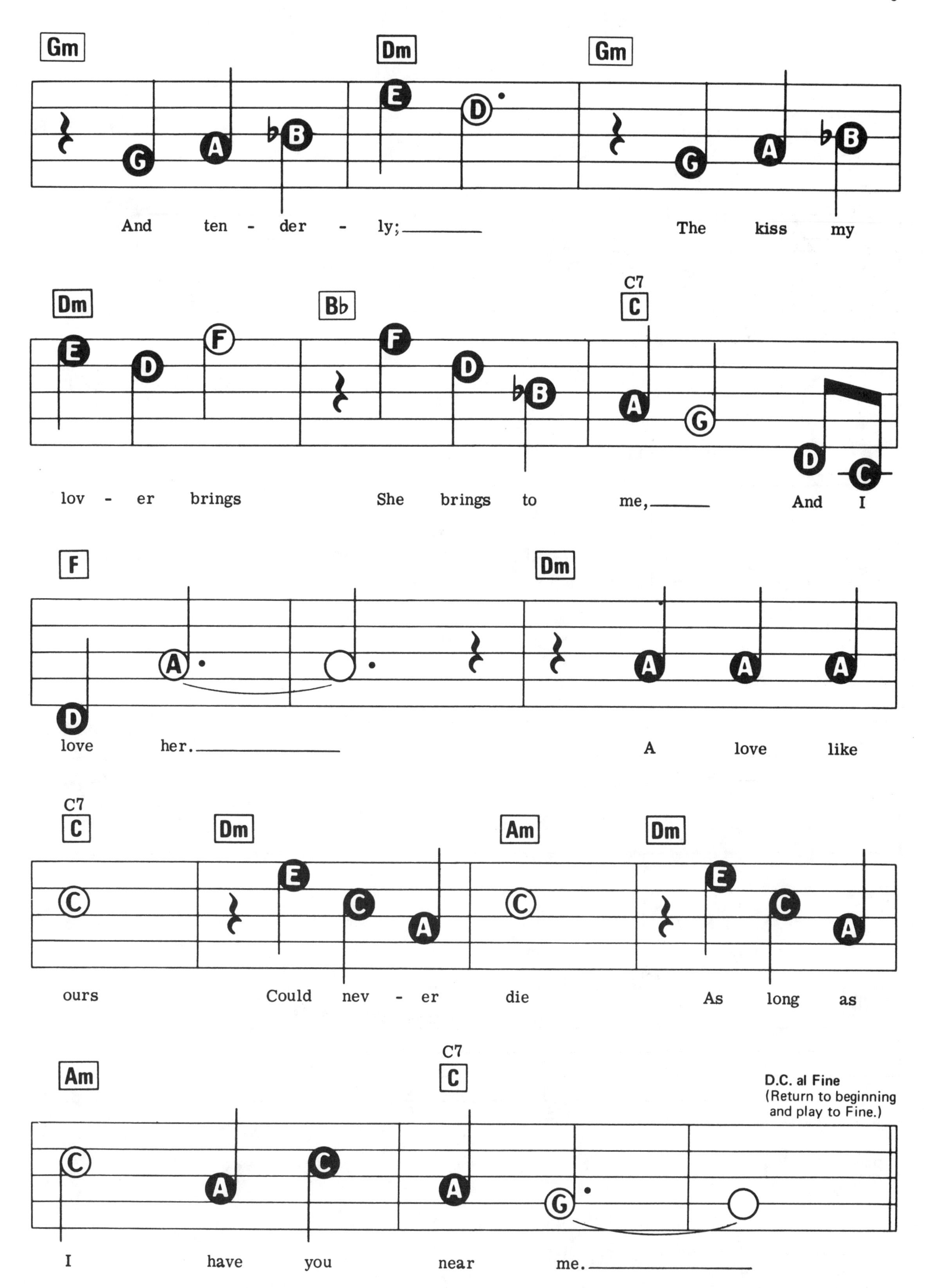
Gm
Dm
Gm
G
A
B
E
D
G
A
B
And ten - der - ly;
The kiss my
Dm
Bb
C7
C
E
D
F
F
D
B
A
G
D
C
lov - er brings
She brings to
me,
And I
F
Dm
D
A
A
A
A
love
her.
A love like
C7
C
Dm
Am
Dm
C
E
C
A
C
E
C
A
ours
Could nev - er die
As long as
Am
C7
C
D.C. al Fine
(Return to beginning and play to Fine.)
C
A
C
A
G
I have you near me.

And I Love You So

Registration 3
Rhythm: Pops or 8 Beat

Words and Music by
Don McLean

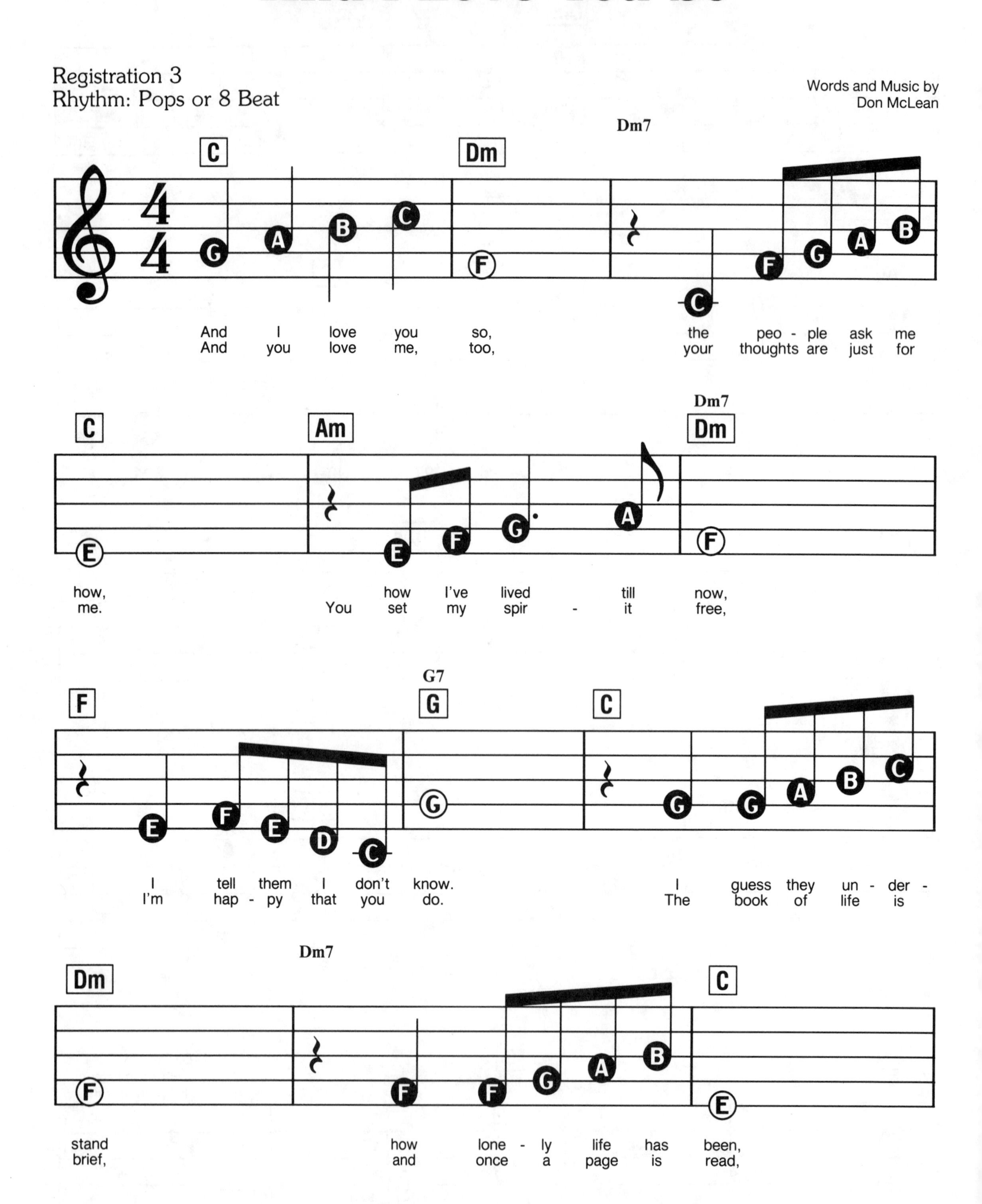

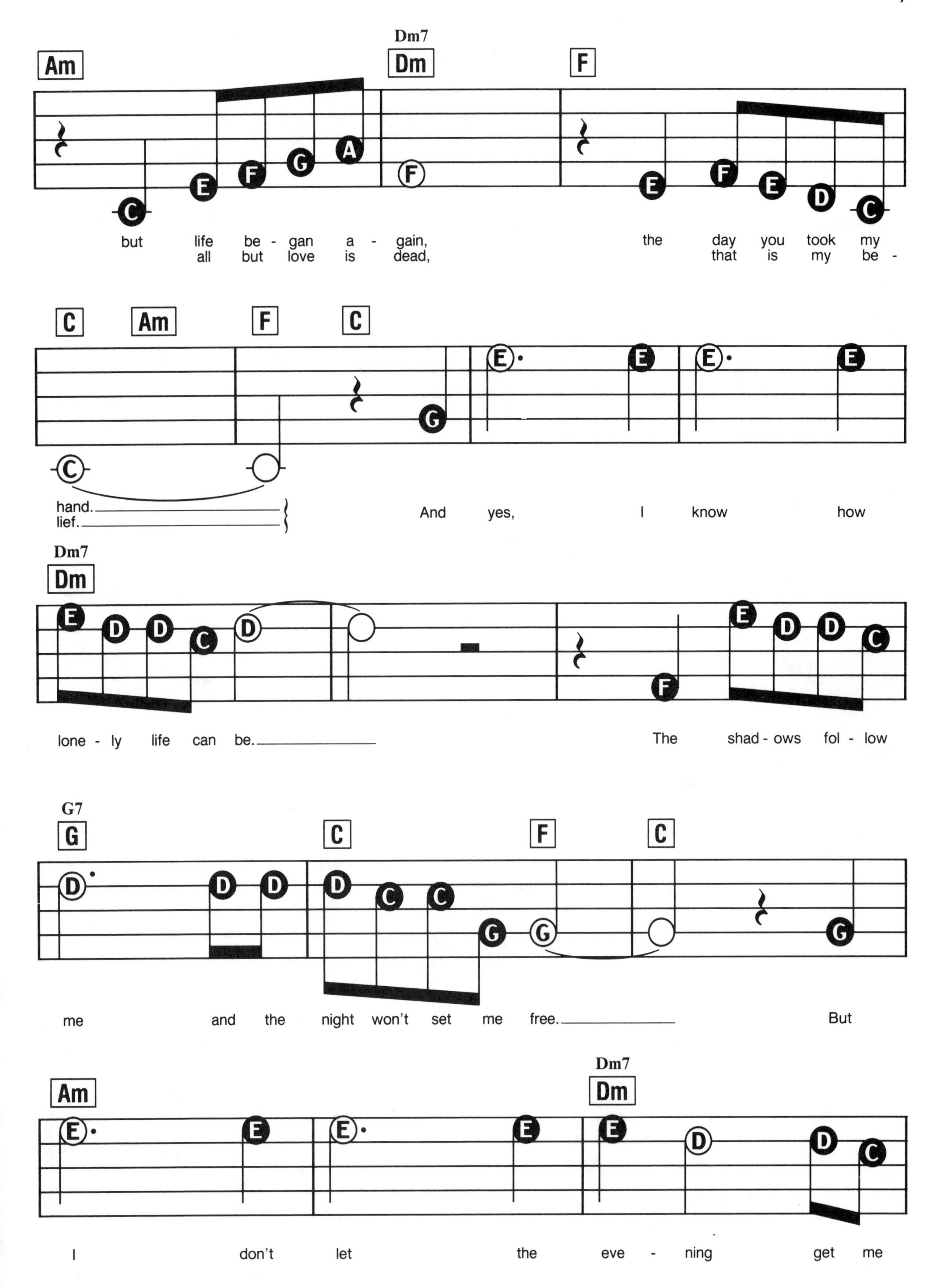
Am
Dm7
Dm
F
but life be - gan a - gain,
all but love is dead,
the day you took my
that is my be -
C
Am
F
C
hand.
lief.
And yes, I know how
Dm7
Dm
lone - ly life can be.
The shad - ows fol - low
G7
G
C
F
C
me and the night won't set me free.
But
Am
Dm7
Dm
I don't let the eve - ning get me

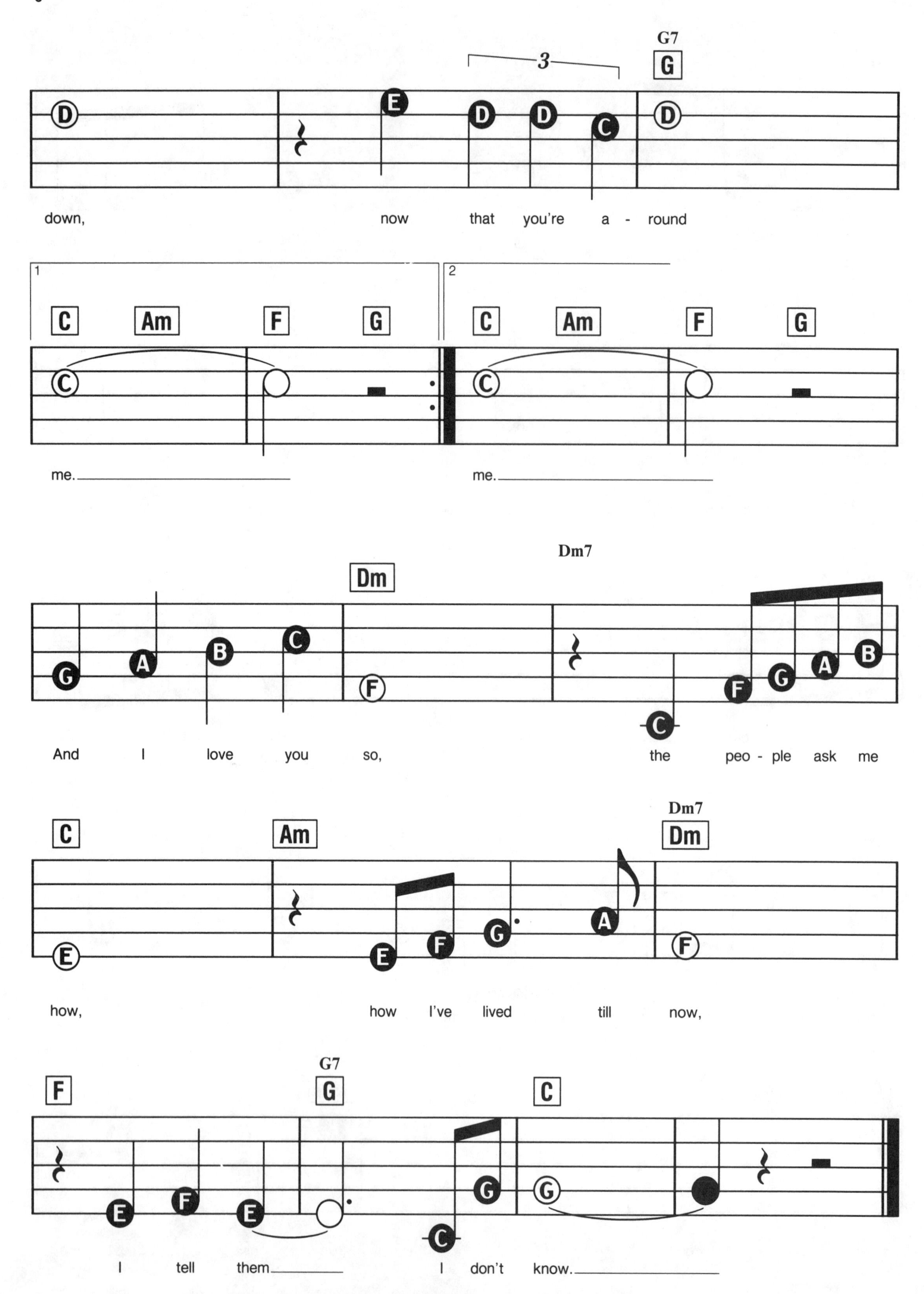
G7
down, now that you're a - round
1
2
C Am F G
me.
me.
Dm
Dm7
And I love you so, the peo - ple ask me
C Am
Dm7
Dm
how, how I've lived till now,
F
G7
G
C
I tell them I don't know.

Can You Feel the Love Tonight

from Walt Disney Pictures' THE LION KING

Registration 2
Rhythm: Rock or 8 Beat

Music by Elton John
Lyrics by Tim Rice

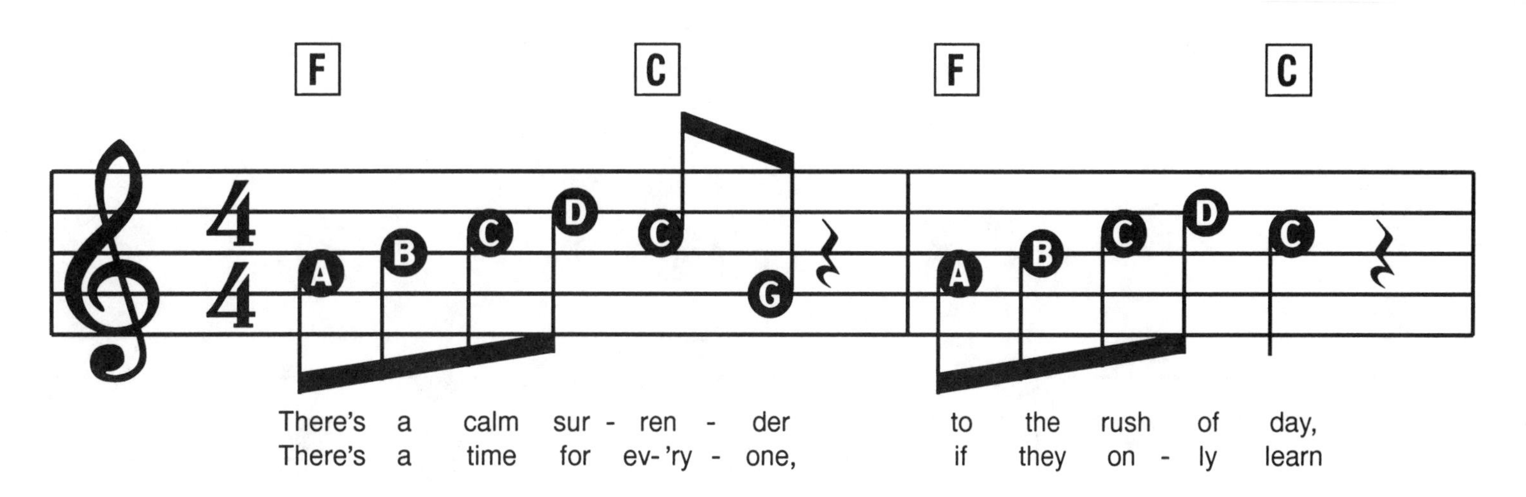

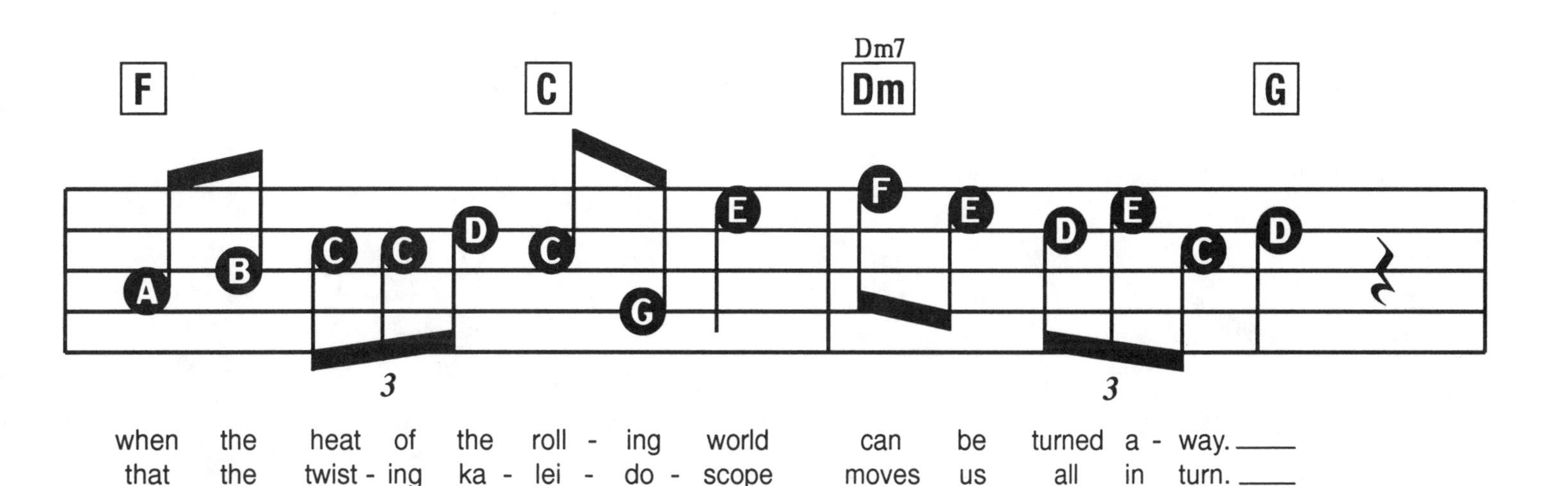

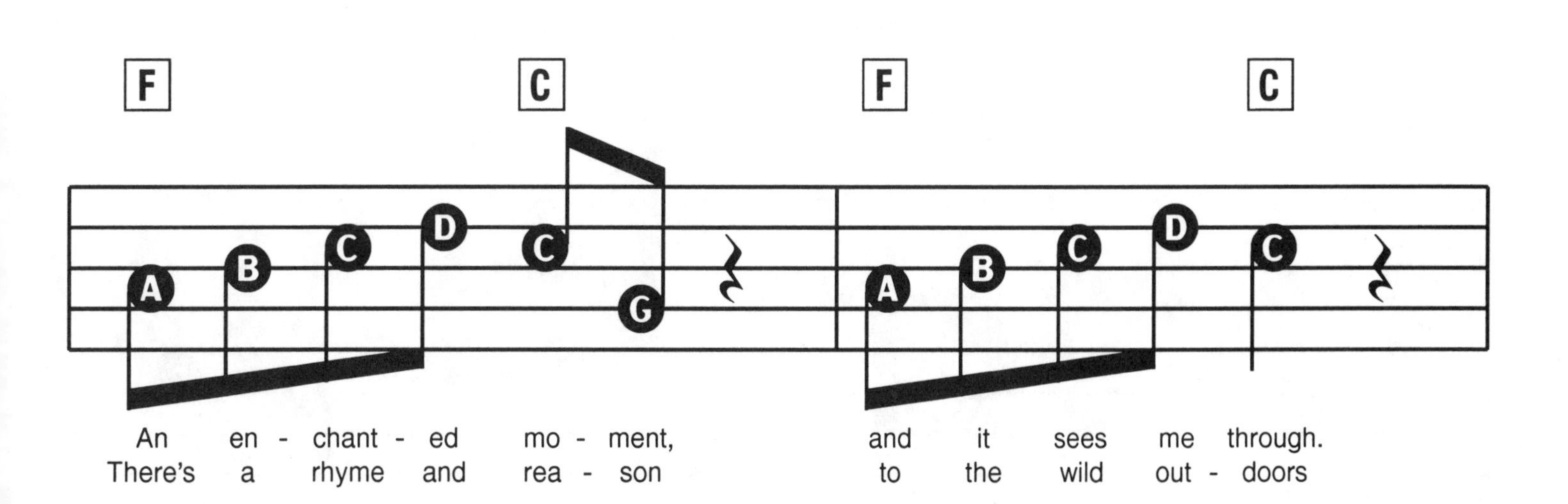

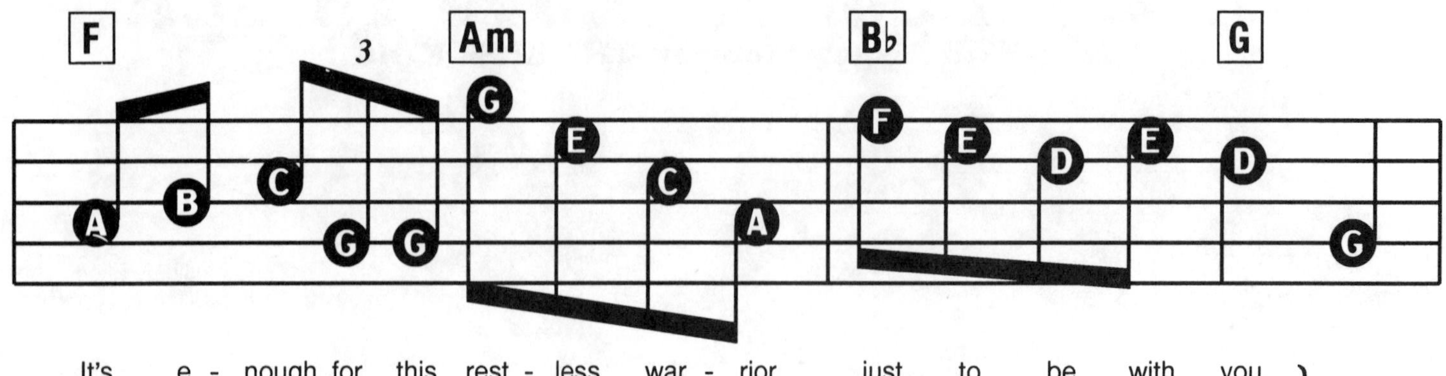
F Am B♭ G
3
It's e - nough for this rest - less war - rior just to be with you.
when the heart of this star - crossed voy - ag - er beats in time with yours.
And

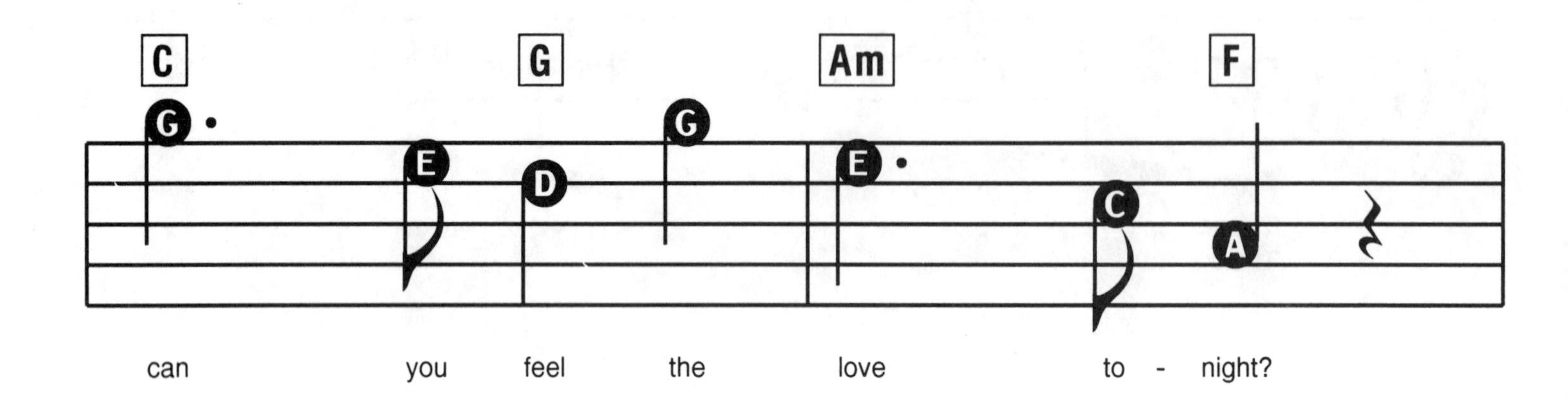
C G Am F
can you feel the love to - night?

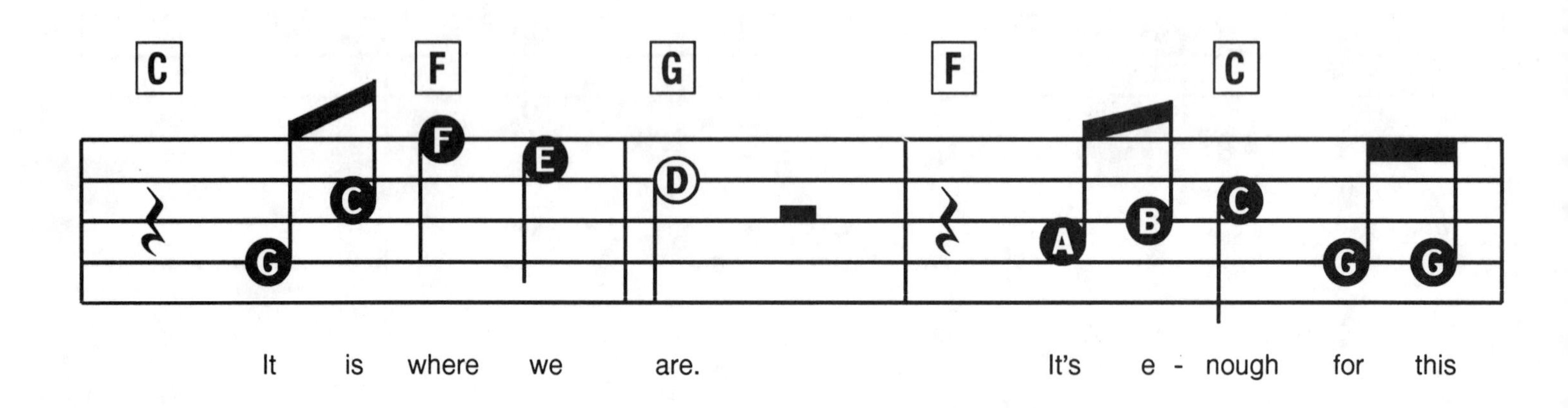
C F G F C
It is where we are. It's e - nough for this

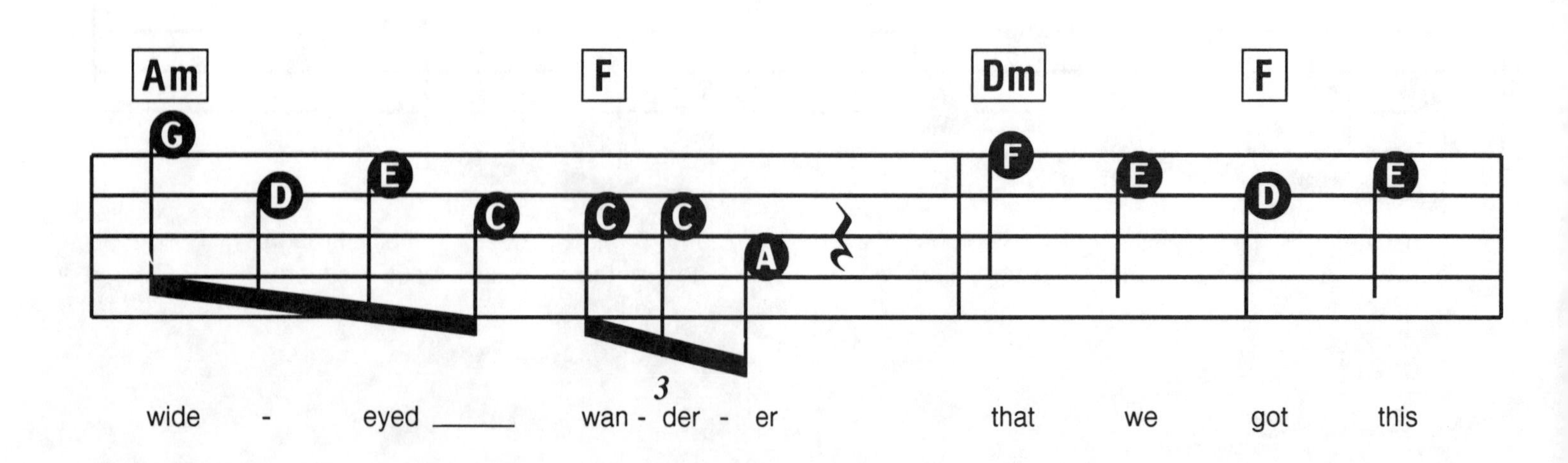
Am F Dm F
3
wide - eyed ____ wan - der - er that we got this

G C G Am F
far. And can you feel the love to - night,
C F G F C
how it's laid to rest? It's e - nough to make
Am F Dm G7 G
kings and vag - a - bonds be - lieve the ver - y
F C F C
best. It's e - nough to make
Am F Dm G7 G F C
kings and vag - a - bonds be - lieve the ver - y best.

Can't Help Falling in Love

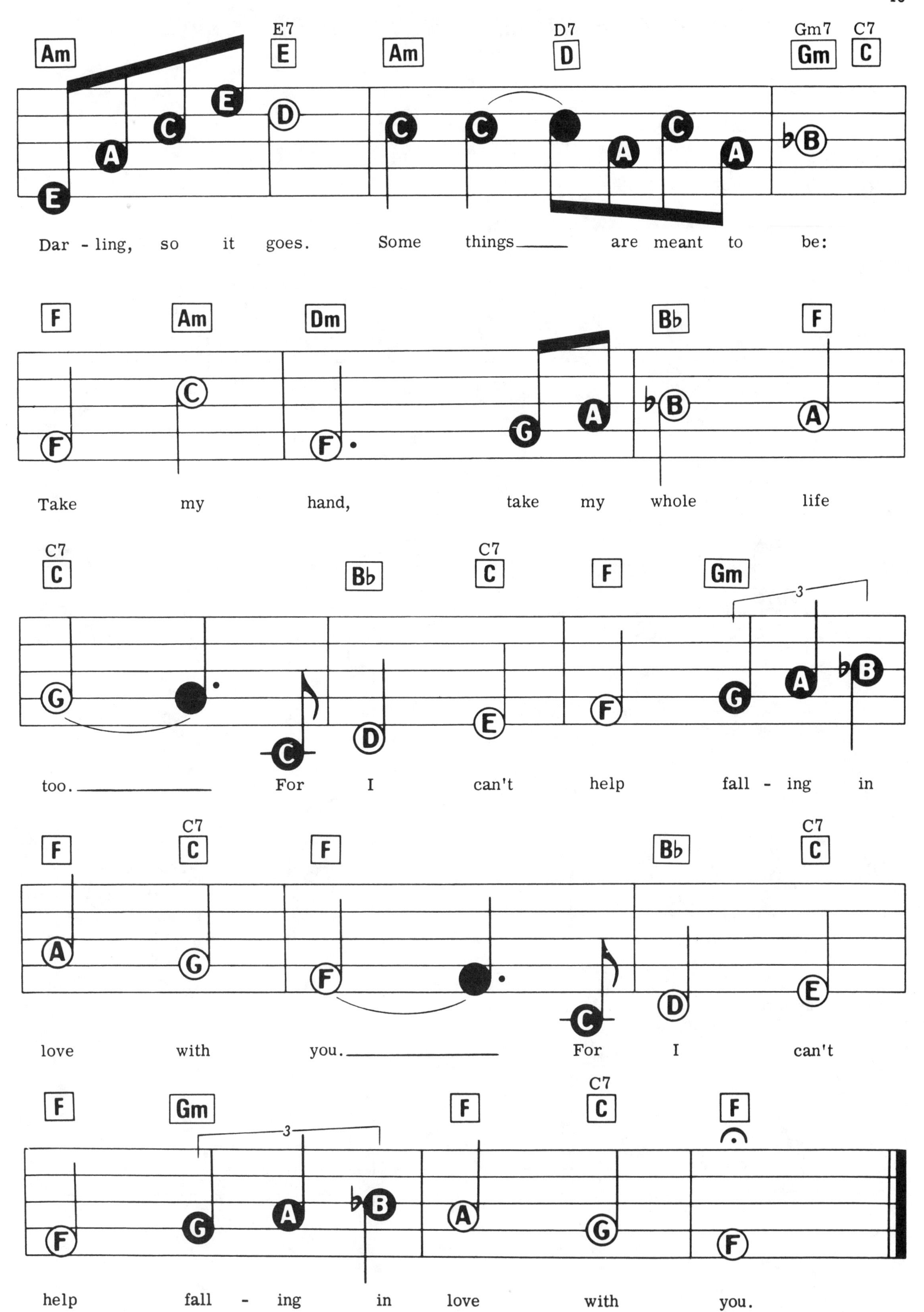
Am E7 E Am D7 D Gm7 Gm C7 C
Dar - ling, so it goes. Some things are meant to be:
F Am Dm Bb F
Take my hand, take my whole life
C7 C Bb C7 C F Gm
too. For I can't help fall - ing in
F C7 C F Bb C7 C
love with you. For I can't
F Gm F C7 C F
help fall - ing in love with you.

Can't Smile without You

Registration 3
Rhythm: Fox Trot or Swing

Words and Music by Chris Arnold,
David Martin and Geoff Morrow

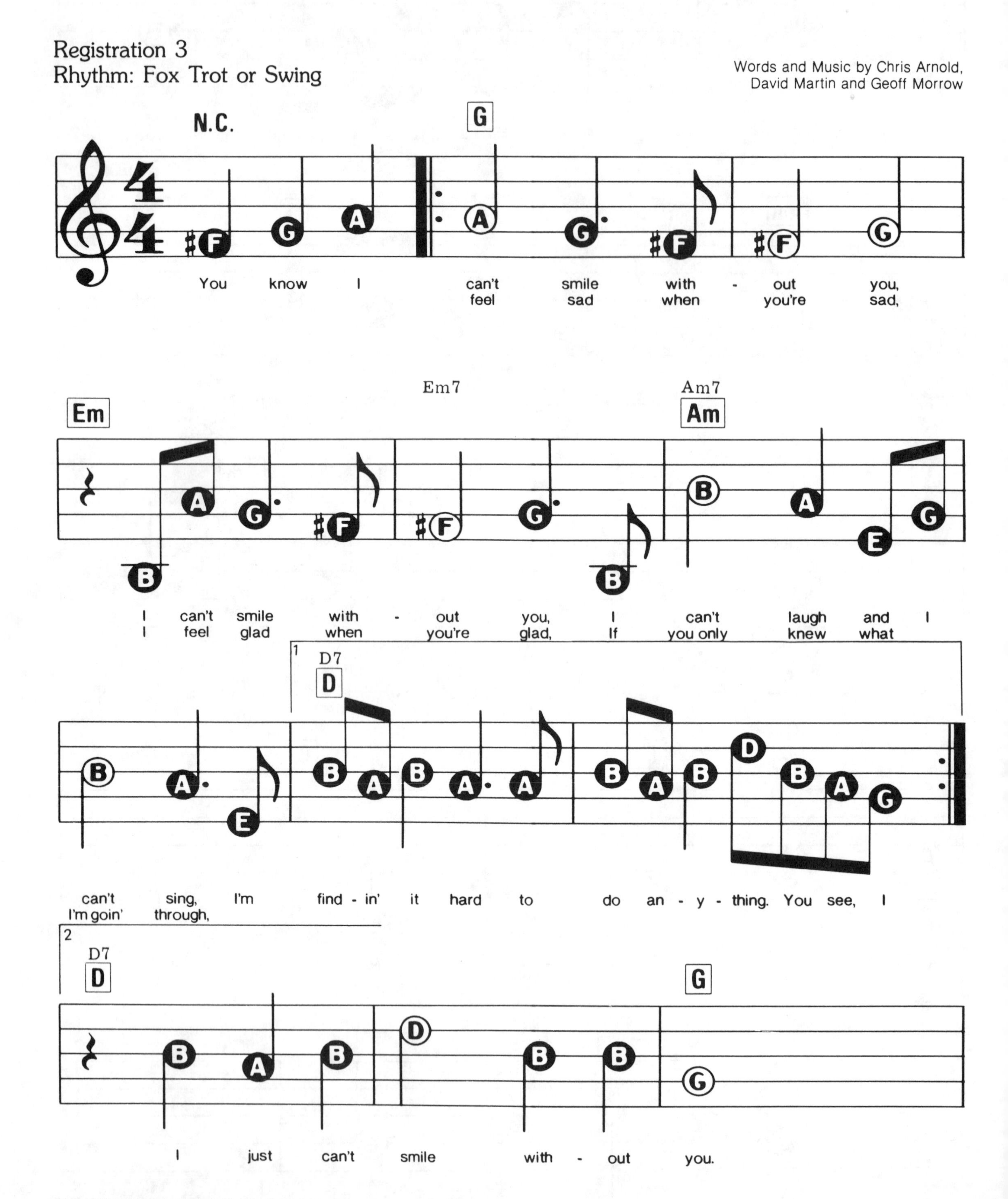

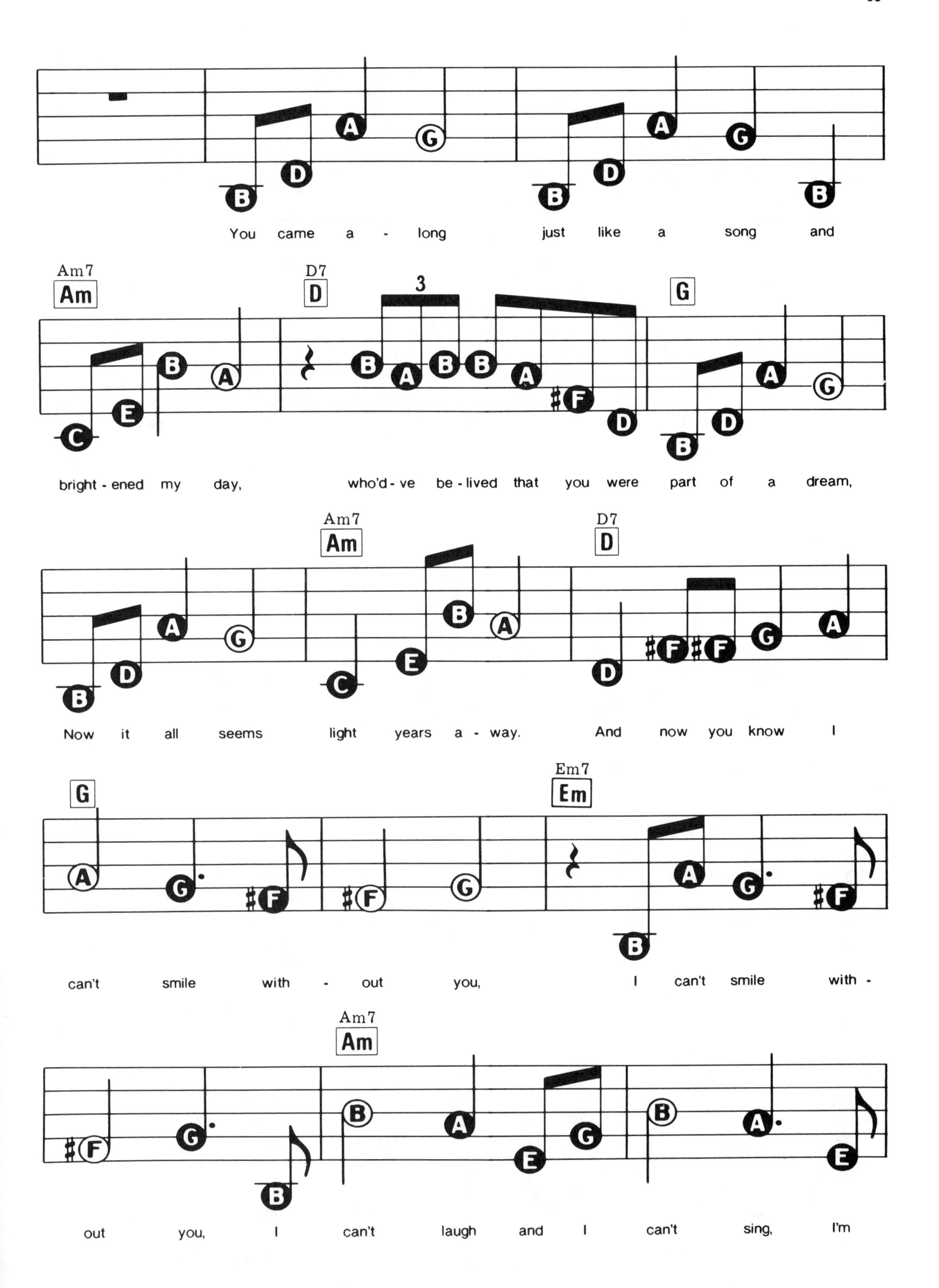

You came a - long just like a song and
Am7
Am
D7
D
3
G
bright - ened my day, who'd - ve be - lived that you were part of a dream,
Am7
Am
D7
D
Now it all seems light years a - way. And now you know I
G
Em7
Em
can't smile with - out you, I can't smile with -
Am7
Am
out you, I can't laugh and I can't sing, I'm

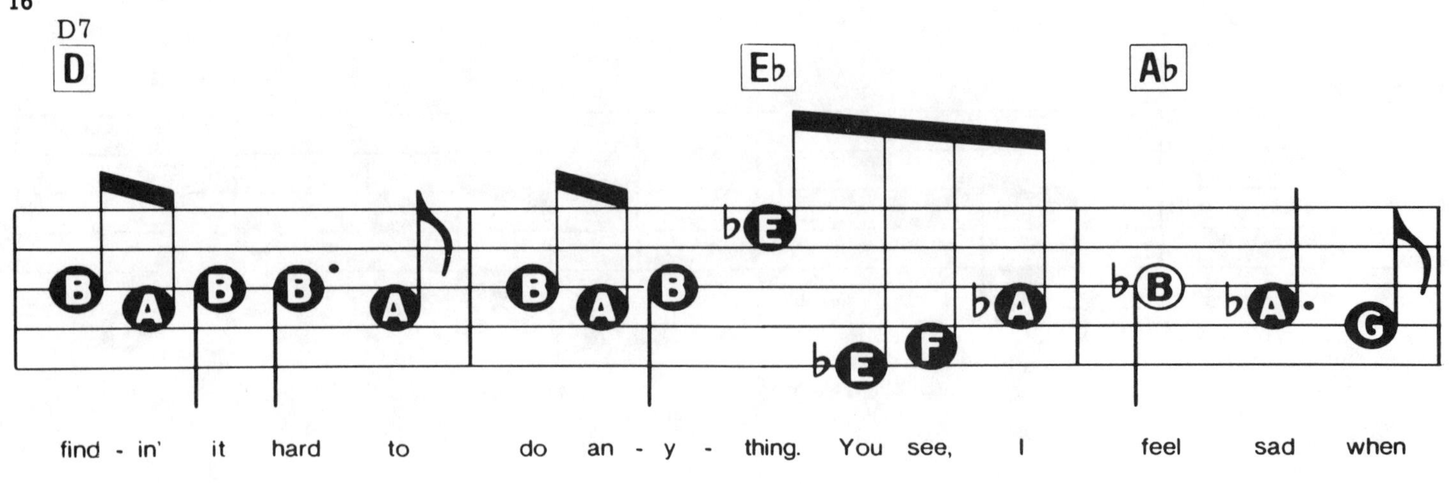
D7
D
Eb
Ab
B A B B A B A B bE bE F bA bB bA G
find - in' it hard to do an - y - thing. You see, I feel sad when

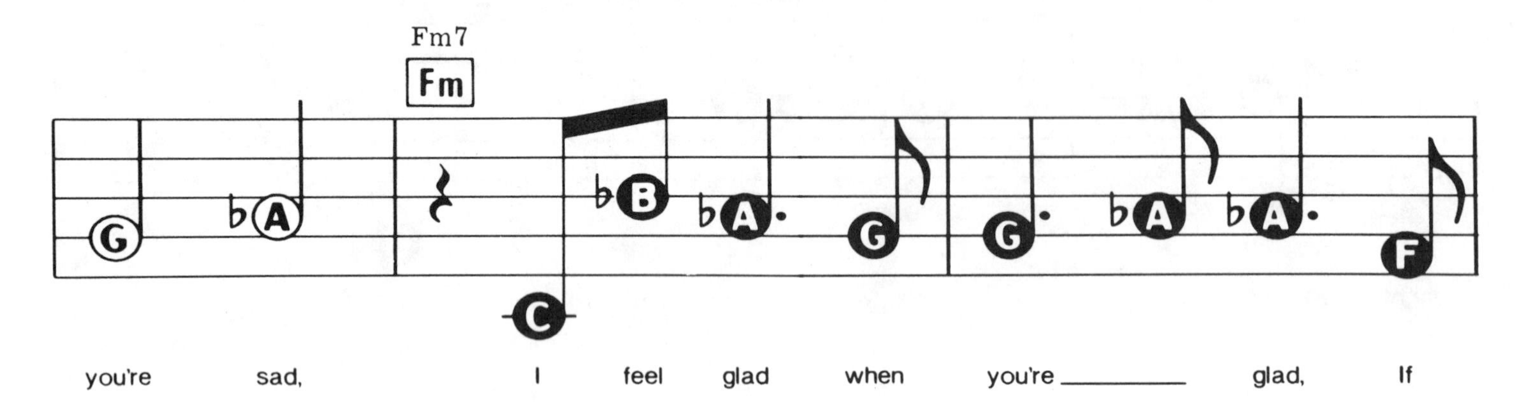
Fm7
Fm
G bA C bB bA G G bA bA F
you're sad, I feel glad when you're glad, If

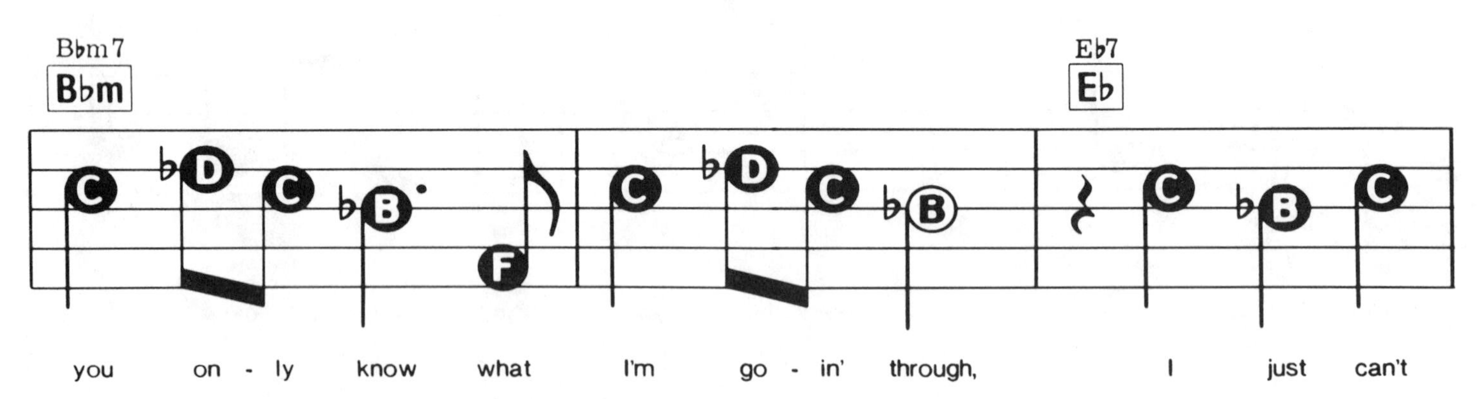
Bbm7
Bbm
Eb7
Eb
C bD C bB F C bD C bB C bB C
you on - ly know what I'm go - in' through, I just can't

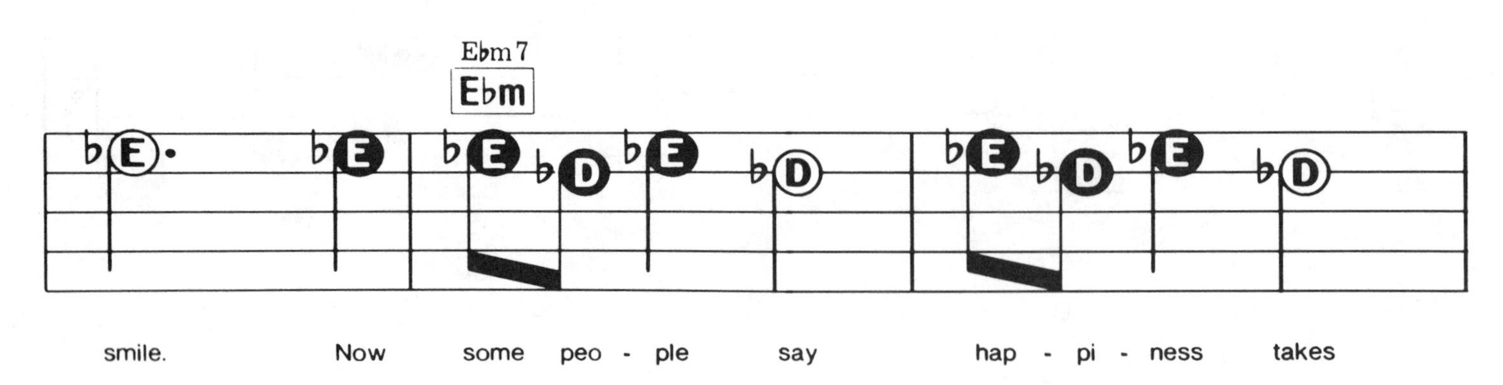
Ebm7
Ebm
bE bE bE bD bE bD bE bD bE bD
smile. Now some peo - ple say hap - pi - ness takes

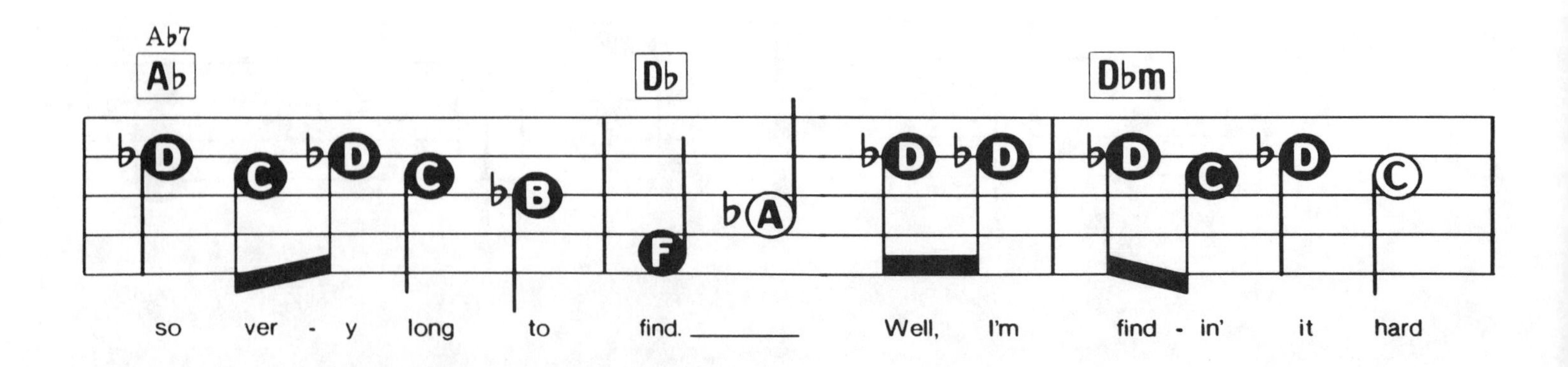
Ab7
Ab
Db
Dbm
bD C bD C bB F bA bD bD bD C bD C
so ver - y long to find. Well, I'm find - in' it hard

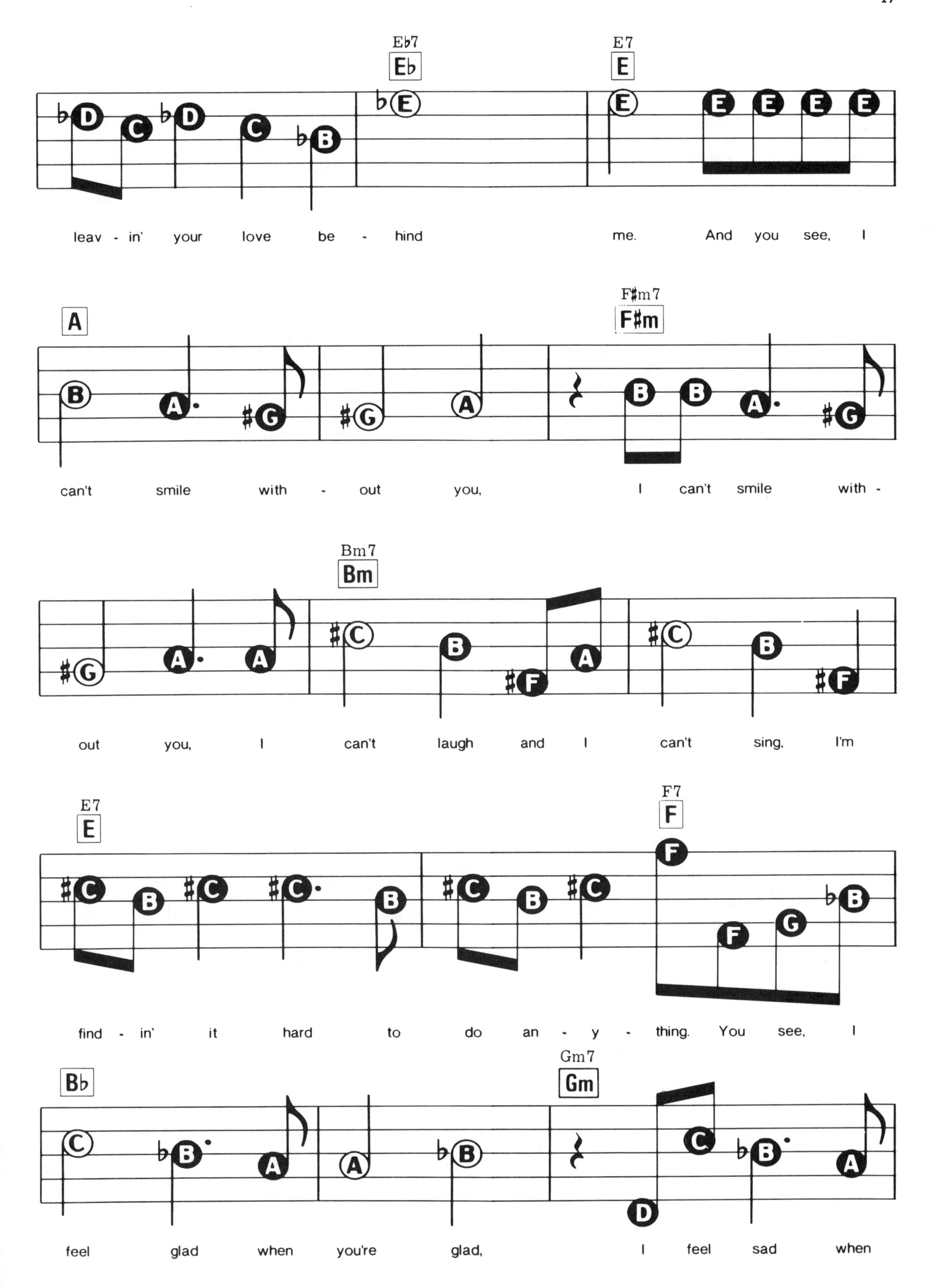

E♭7 E♭ E7 E
leav - in' your love be - hind me. And you see, I
A F♯m7 F♯m
can't smile with - out you, I can't smile with -
Bm7 Bm
out you, I can't laugh and I can't sing, I'm
E7 E F7 F
find - in' it hard to do an - y - thing. You see, I
B♭ Gm7 Gm
feel glad when you're glad, I feel sad when

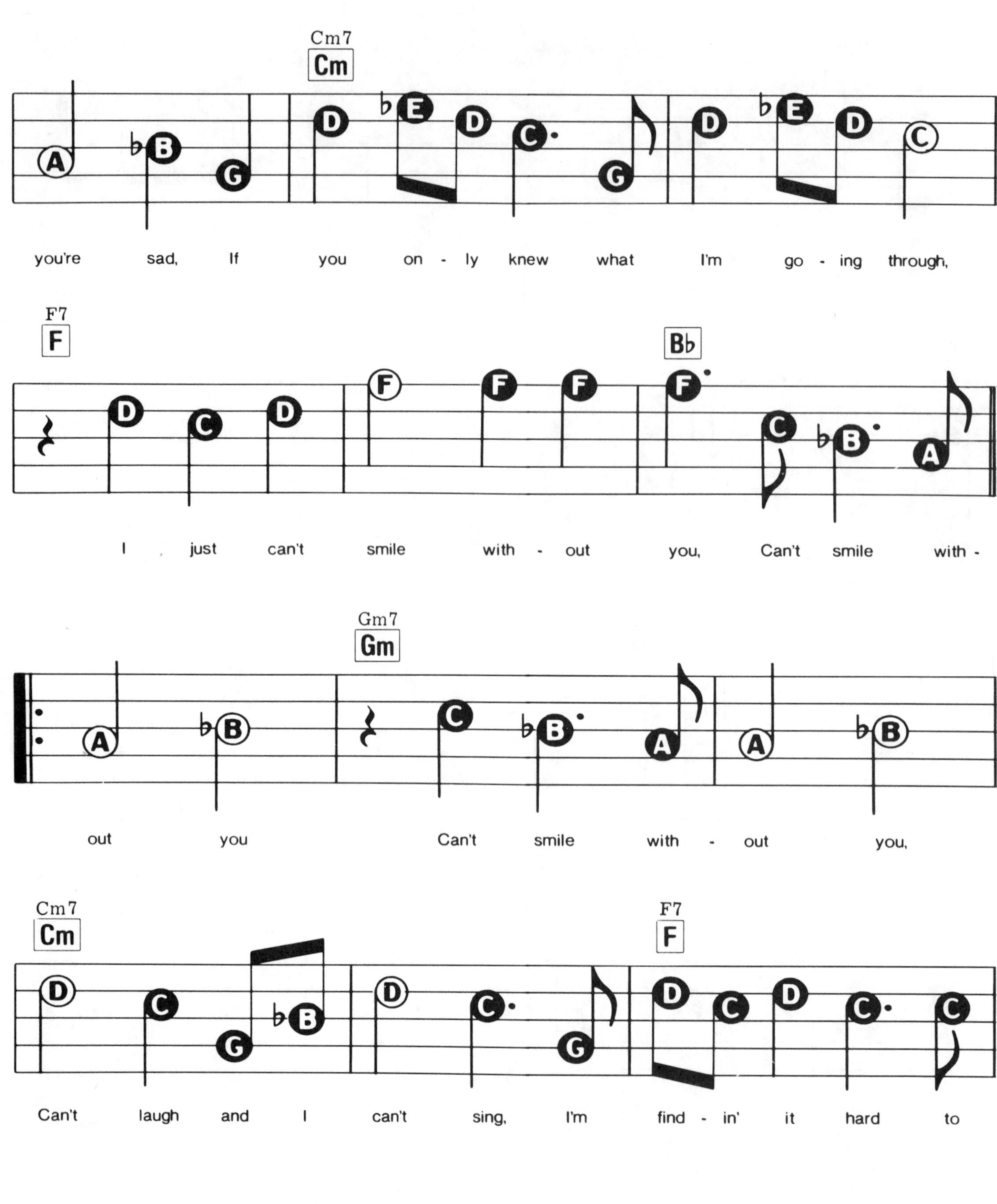
Cm7
Cm
you're sad, If you on - ly knew what I'm go - ing through,
F7
F
Bb
I just can't smile with - out you, Can't smile with -
Gm7
Gm
out you Can't smile with - out you,
Cm7
Cm
F7
F
Can't laugh and I can't sing, I'm find - in' it hard to

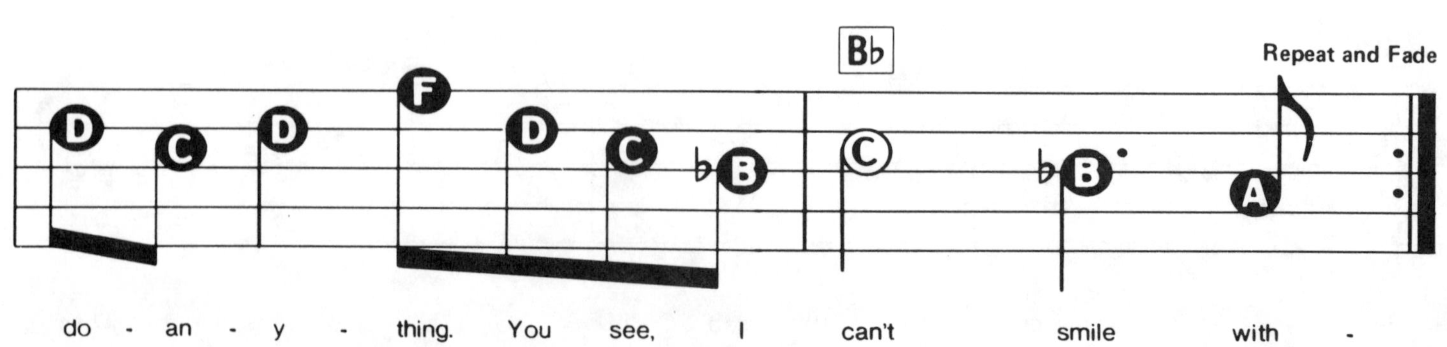
Bb
Repeat and Fade
do - an - y - thing. You see, I can't smile with -

(They Long to Be)
Close to You

Registration 2
Rhythm: Slow Rock

Lyric by Hal David
Music by Burt Bacharach

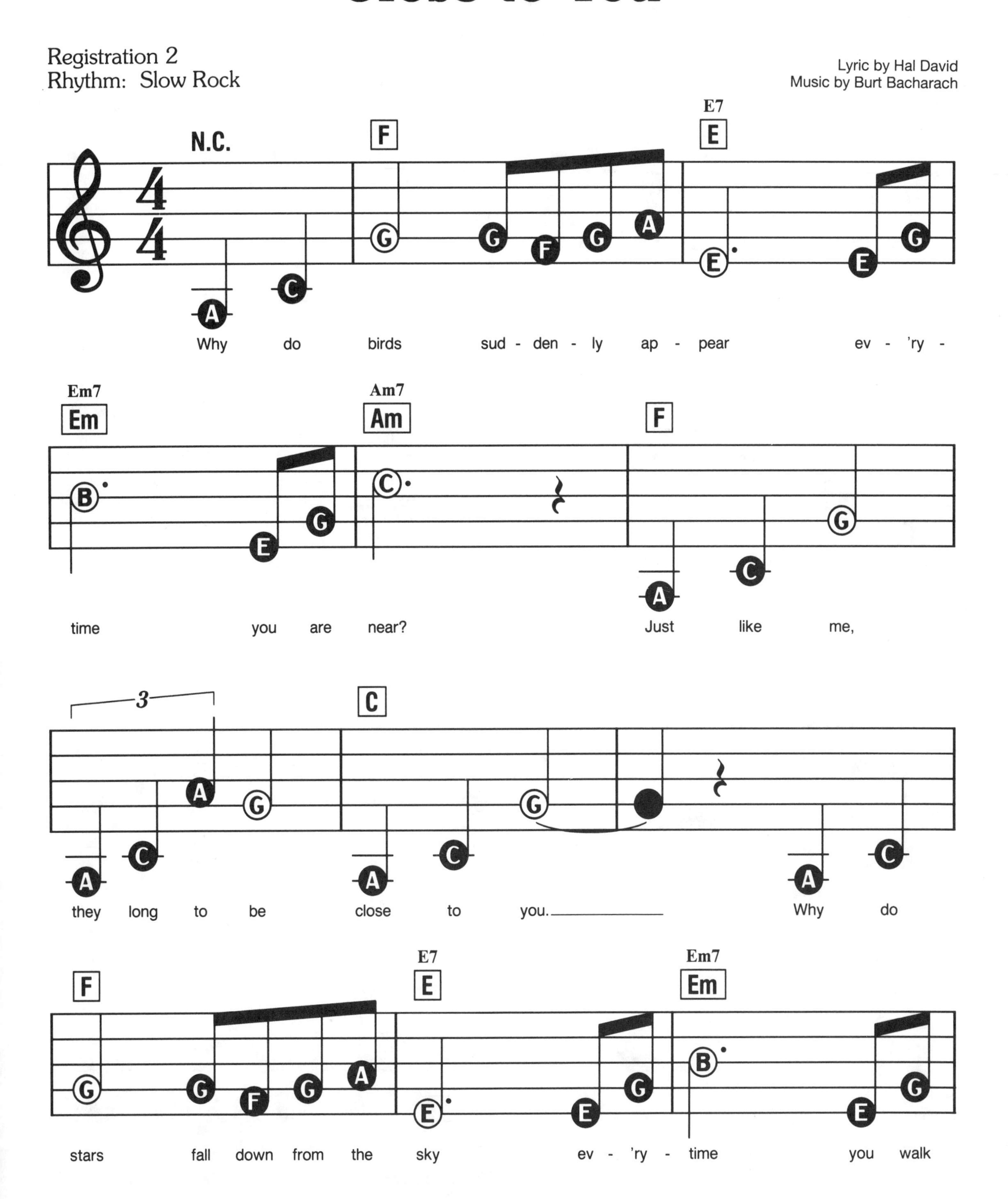

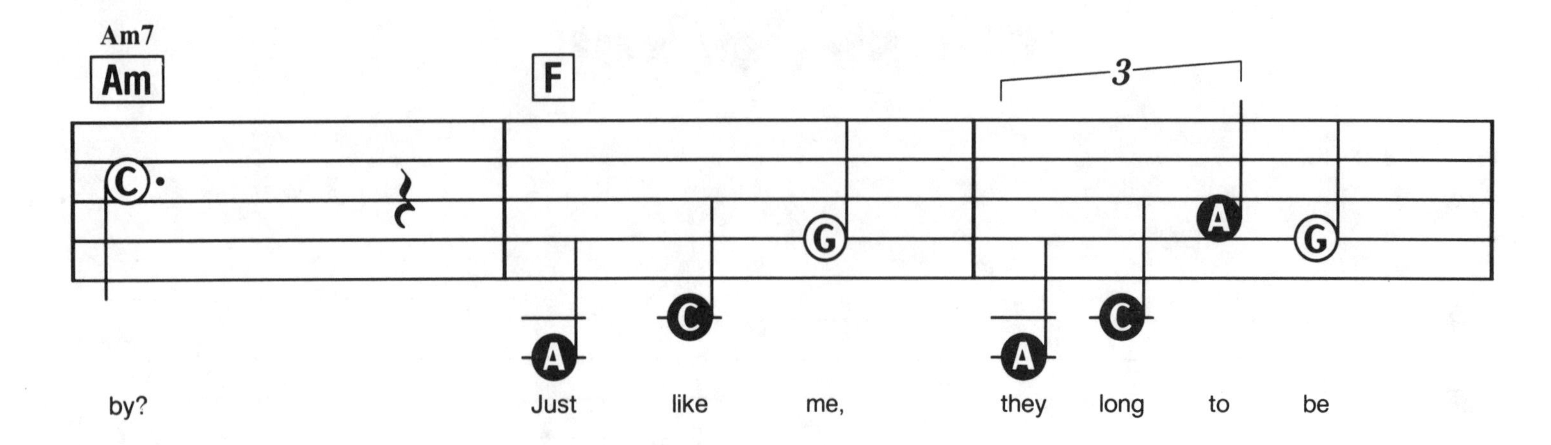
Am7
Am
F
3
C
A
C
G
A
C
A
G
by?
Just like me,
they long to be

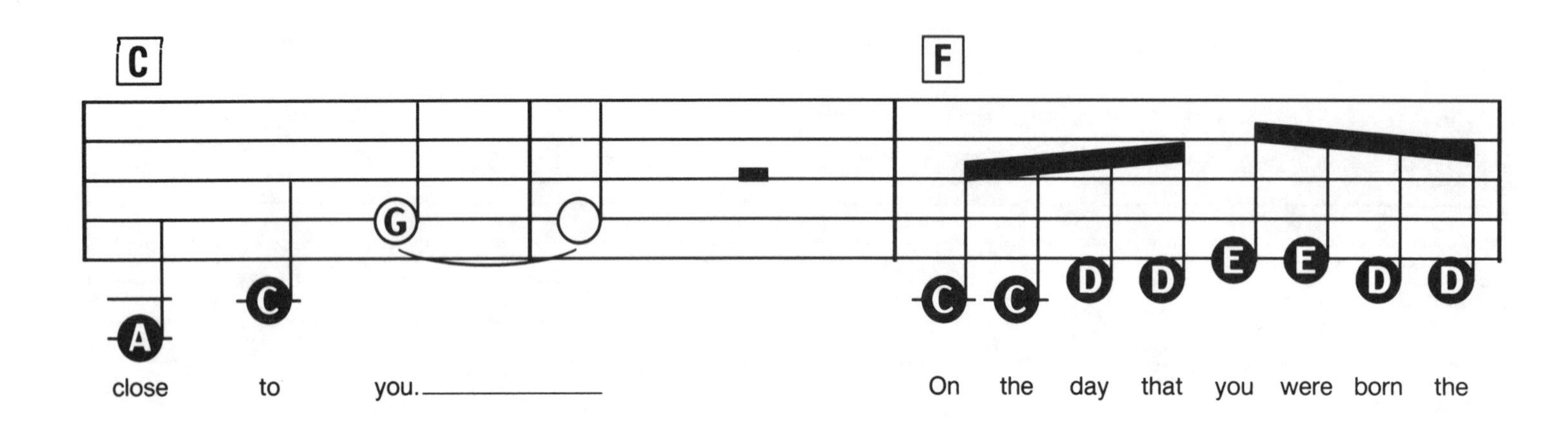
C
F
A
C
G
C C D D E E D D
close to you.
On the day that you were born the

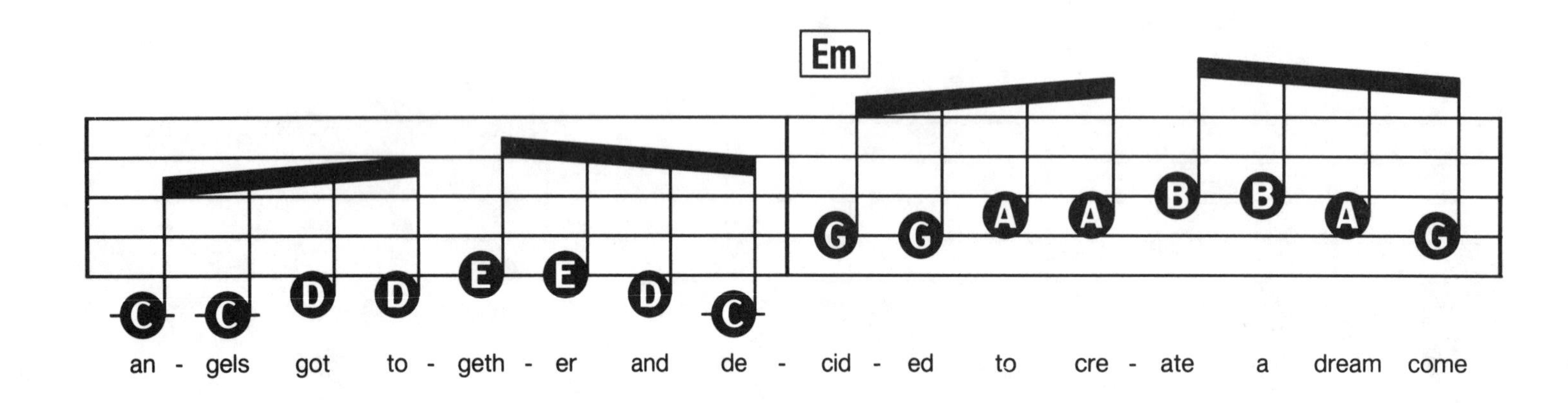
Em
C C D D E E D C
G G A A B B A G
an - gels got to - geth - er and de - cid - ed to cre - ate a dream come

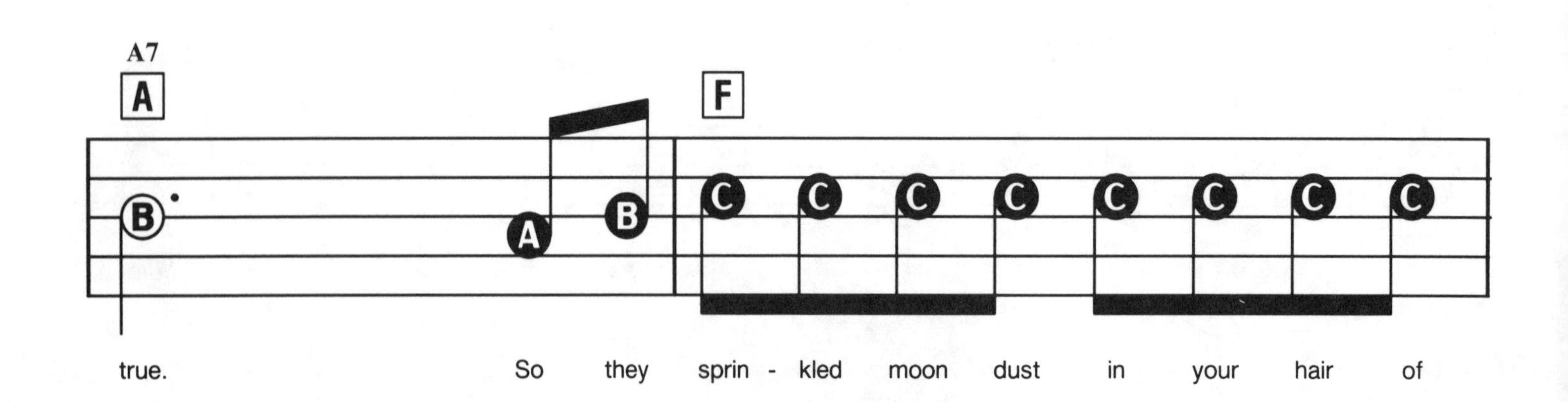
A7
A
F
B
A B
C C C C C C C C
true.
So they sprin - kled moon dust in your hair of

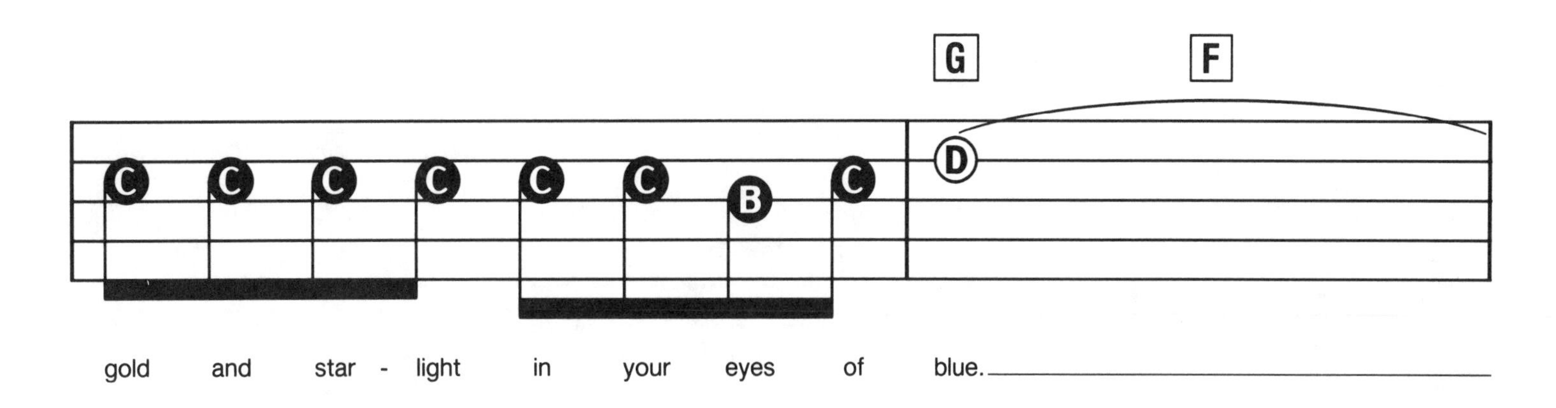
G
F
C
C
C
C
C
C
B
C
D
gold and star - light in your eyes of blue.

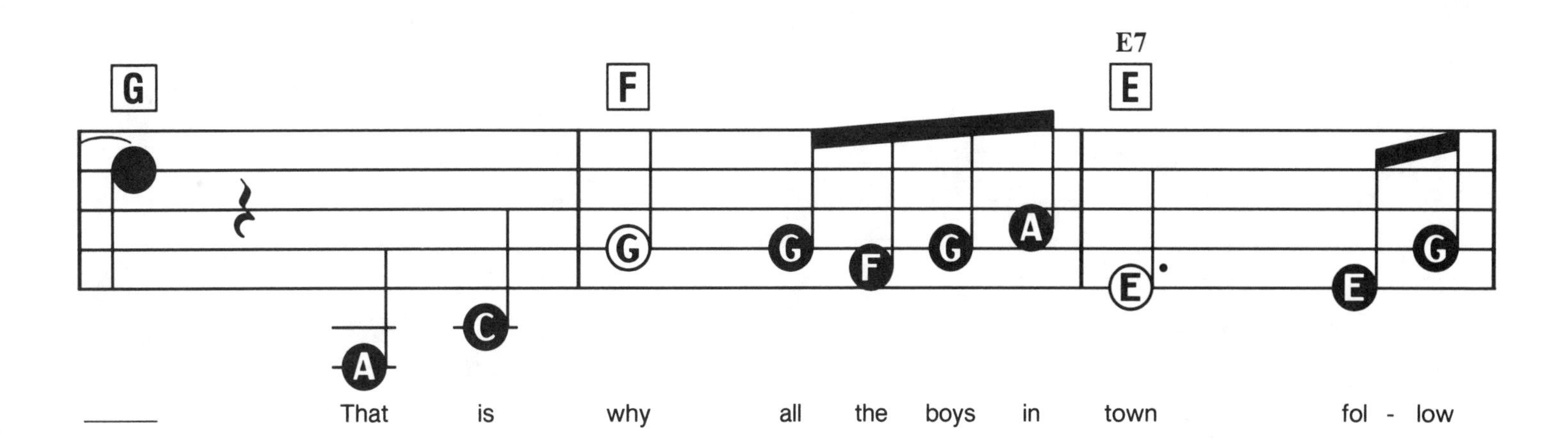
G
F
E7
E
A
C
G
G
F
G
A
E
E
G
That is why all the boys in town fol - low

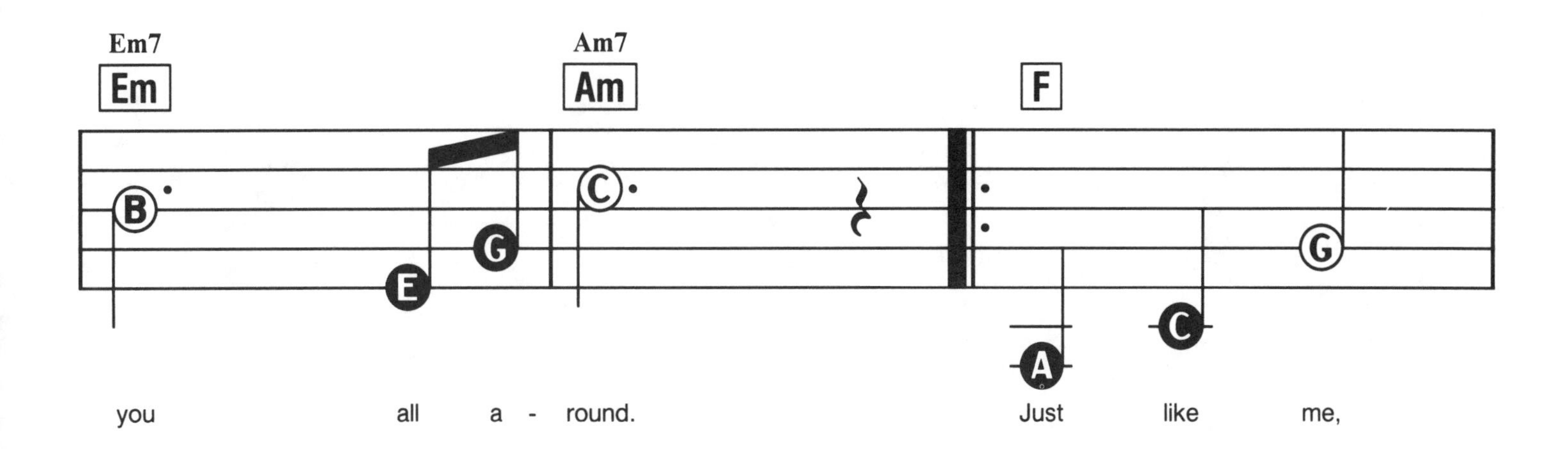
Em7
Em
Am7
Am
F
B
E
G
C
A
C
G
you all a - round. Just like me,

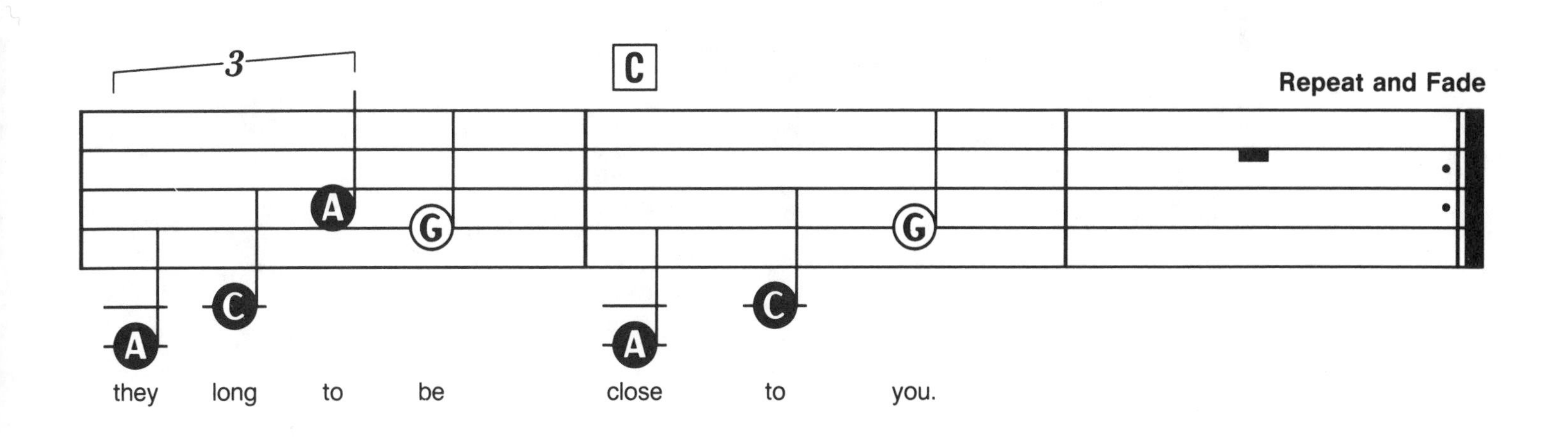
3
C
Repeat and Fade
A
C
A
G
A
C
G
they long to be close to you.

Could I Have This Dance

Registration 4
Rhythm: Waltz

Words and Music by Wayland Holyfield
and Bob House

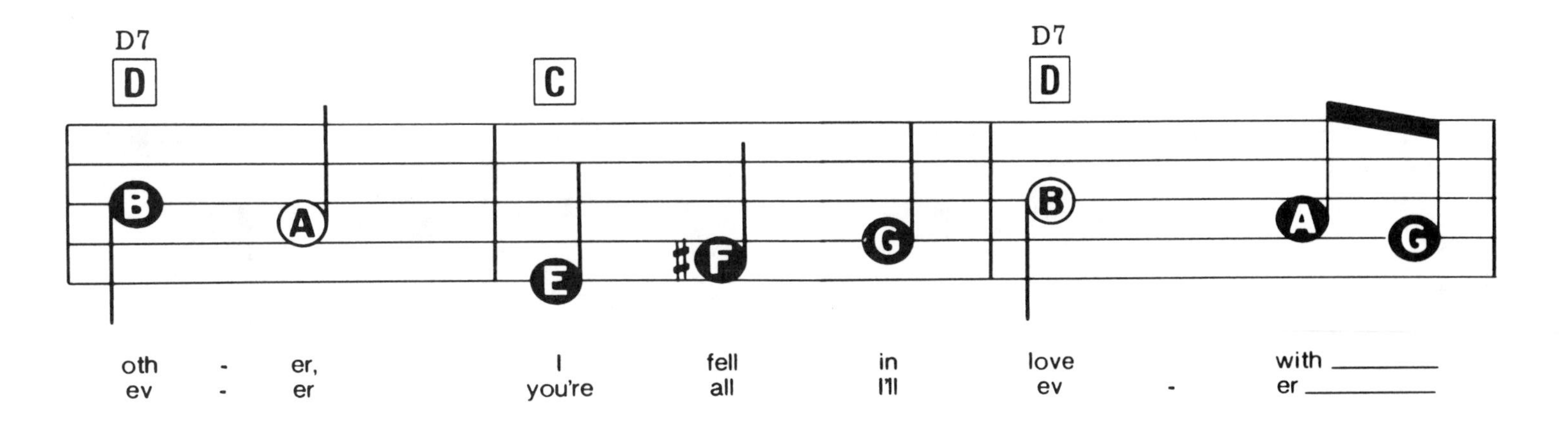
D7
D
C
D7
D
B
A
E
F
G
B
A
G
oth - er,
ev - er
I
you're
fell
all
in
I'll
love
ev - er
with

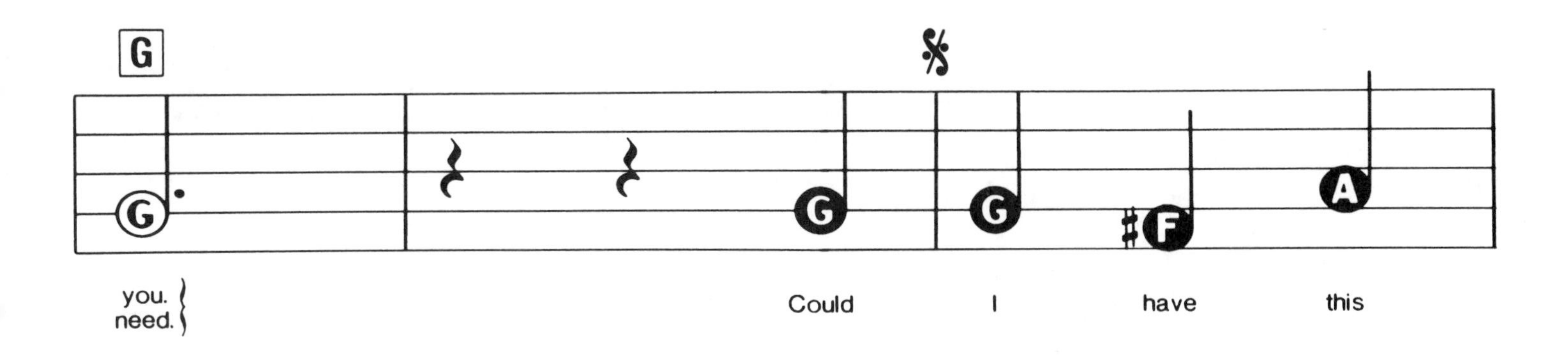
G
G
G
G
F
A
you.
need.
Could
I
have
this

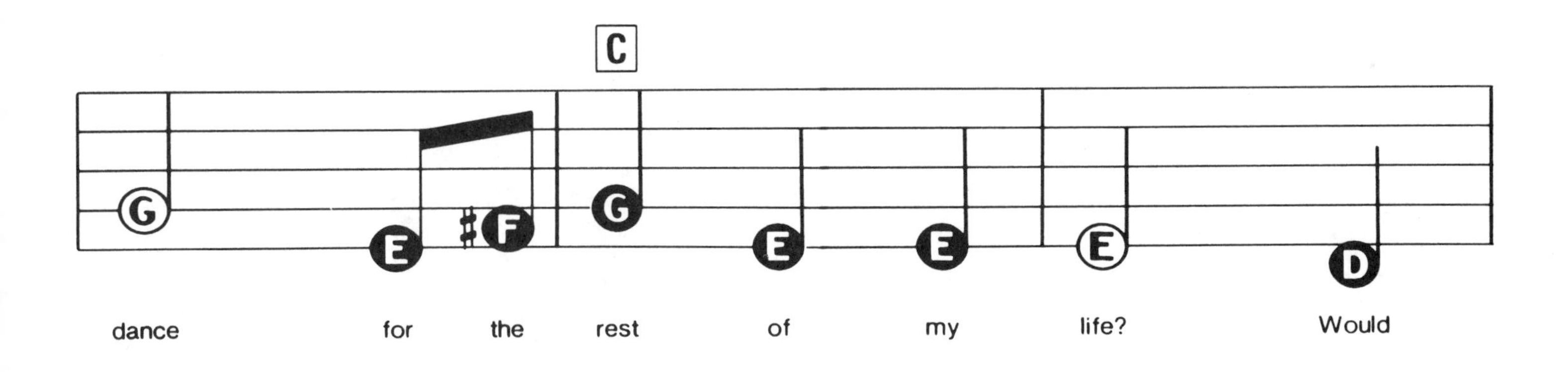
C
G
E
F
G
E
E
E
D
dance
for
the
rest
of
my
life?
Would

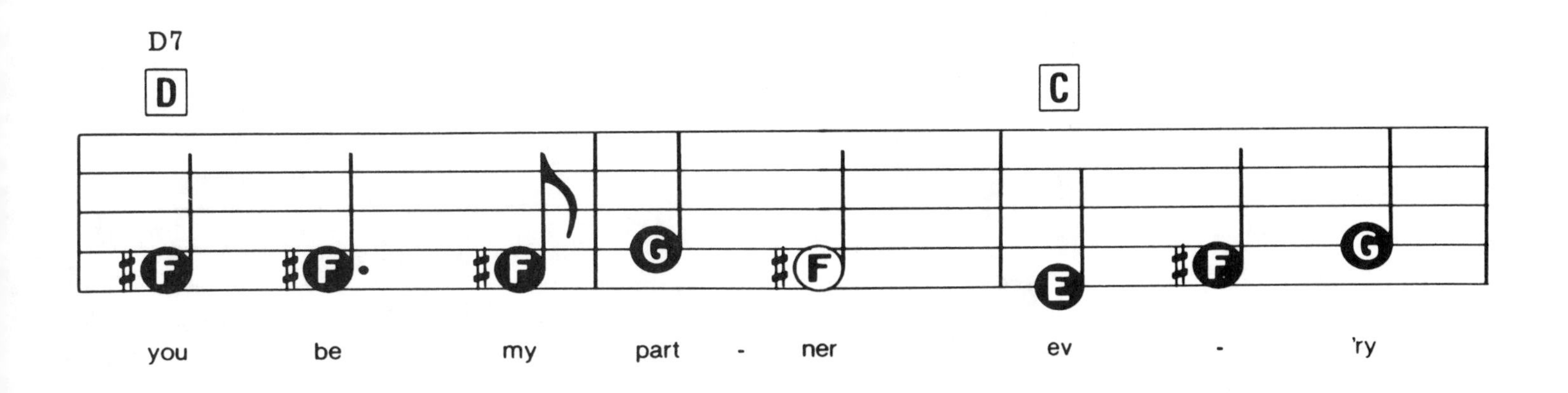
D7
D
C
F
F
F
G
F
E
F
G
you
be
my
part - ner
ev - 'ry

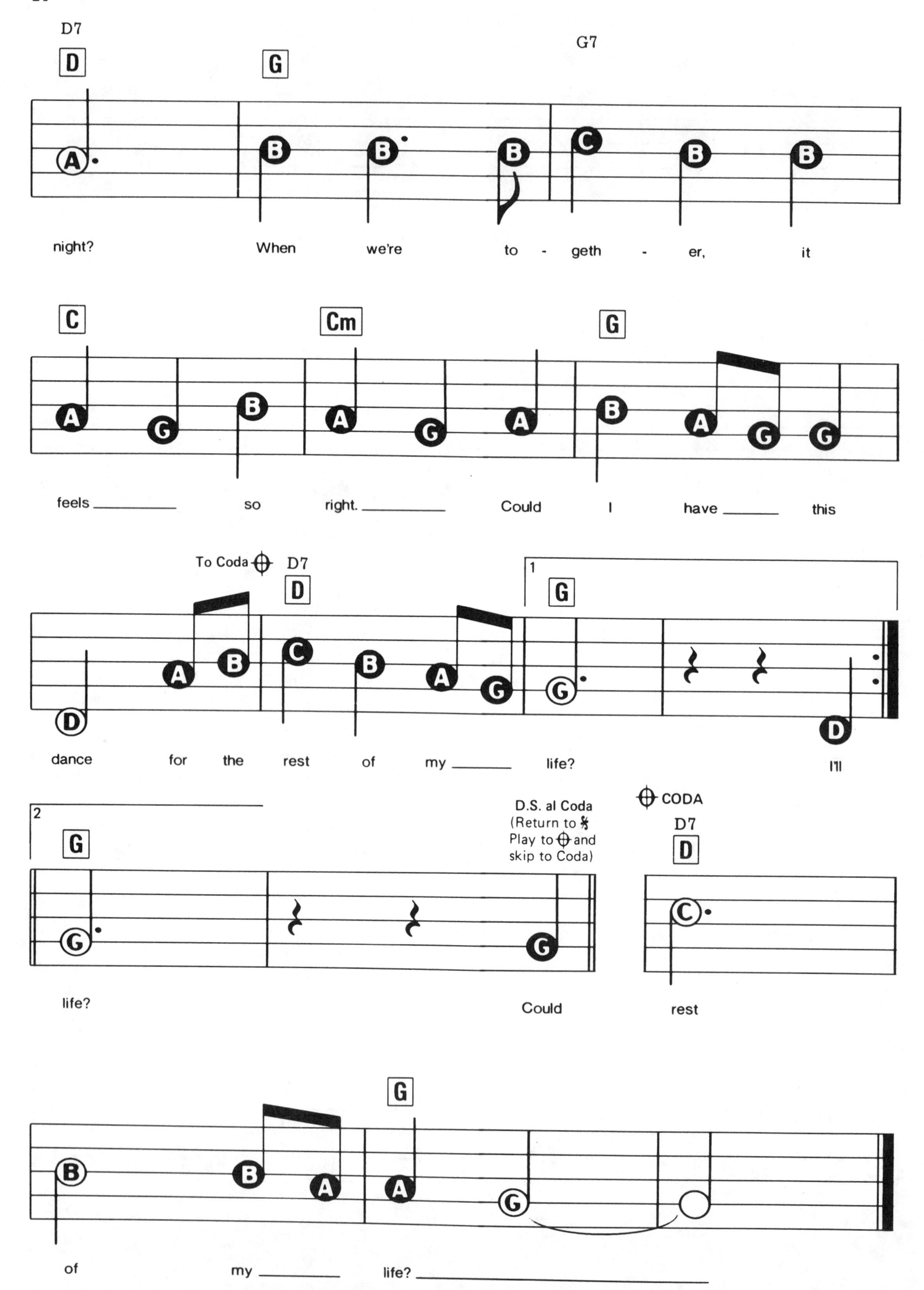
D7
D
G
G7
A B B B C B B
night? When we're to - geth - er, it
C
Cm
G
A G B A G A B A G G
feels so right. Could I have this
To Coda
D7
D
1
G
D A B C B A G G D
dance for the rest of my life? I'll
2
G
D.S. al Coda
(Return to
Play to
and
skip to Coda)
CODA
D7
D
G G C
life? Could rest
G
B B A A G
of my life?

Feelings
(¿Dime?)

Registration 5
Rhythm: Slow Rock

English Words and Music by Morris Albert
Spanish Lyric by Thomas Fundora

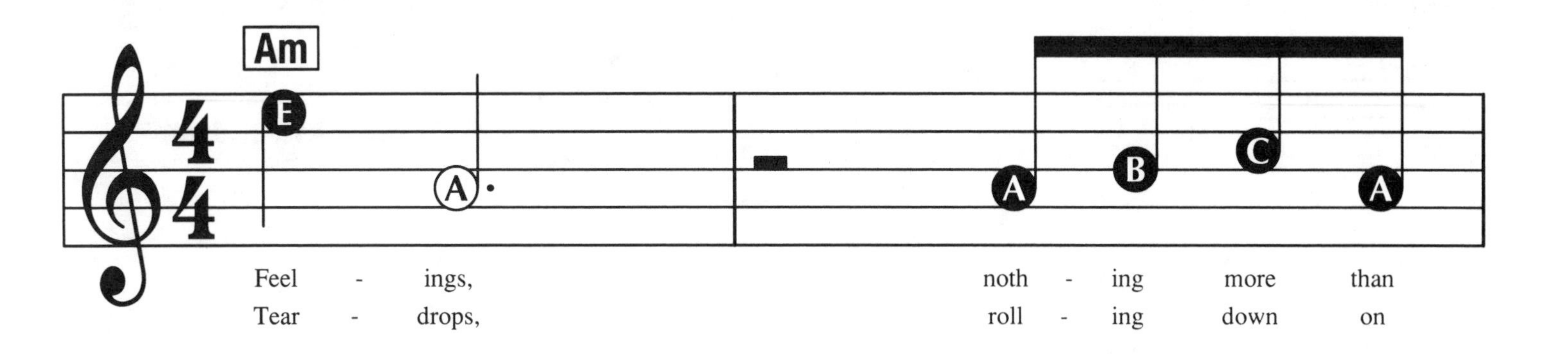

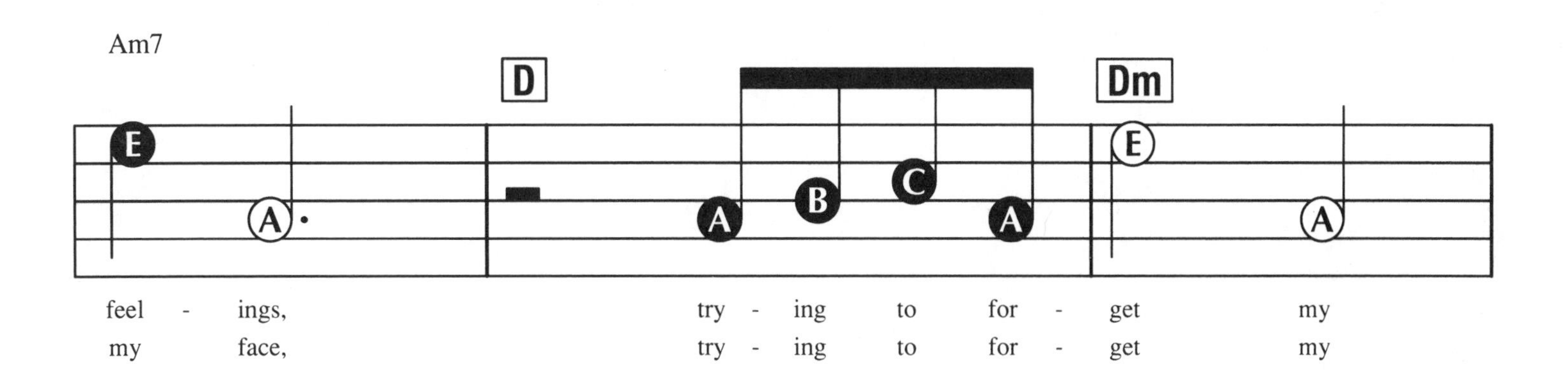

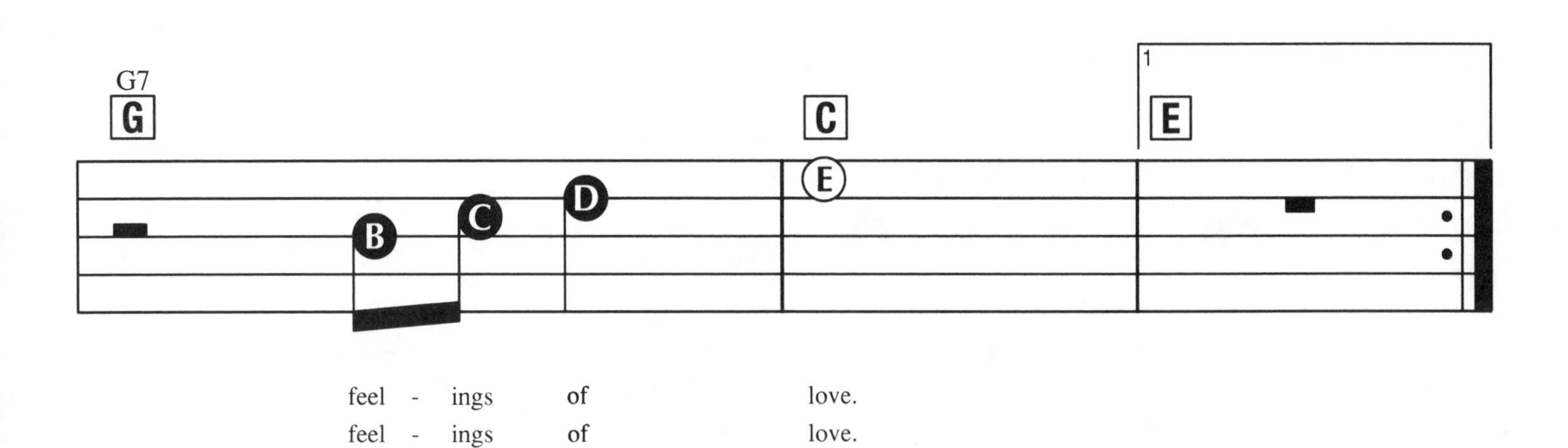

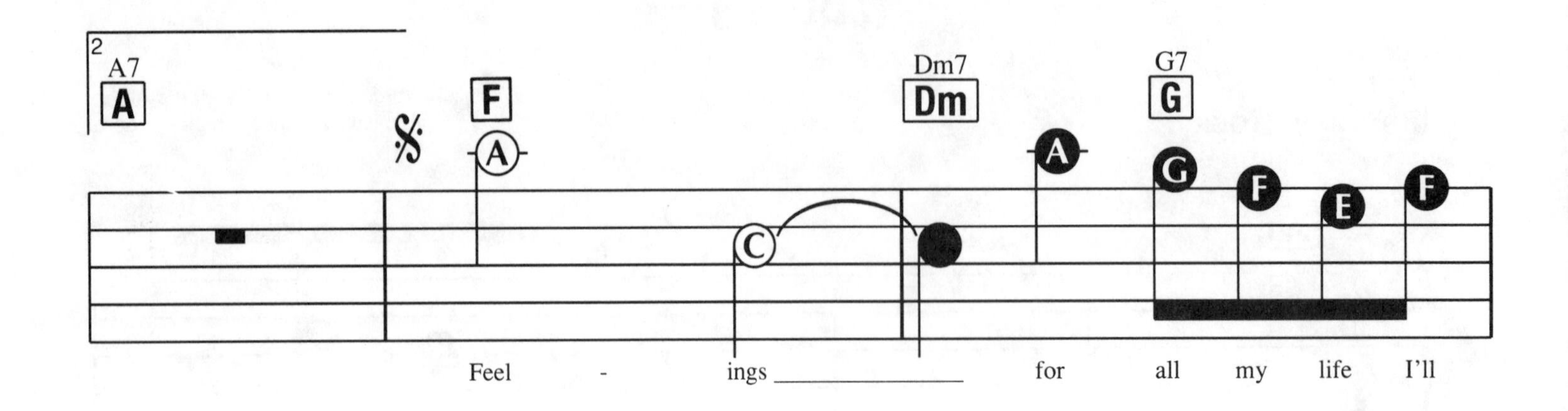
2
A7
A
F
A
C
Dm7
Dm
A
G7
G
G
F
E
F
Feel - ings ______ for all my life I'll

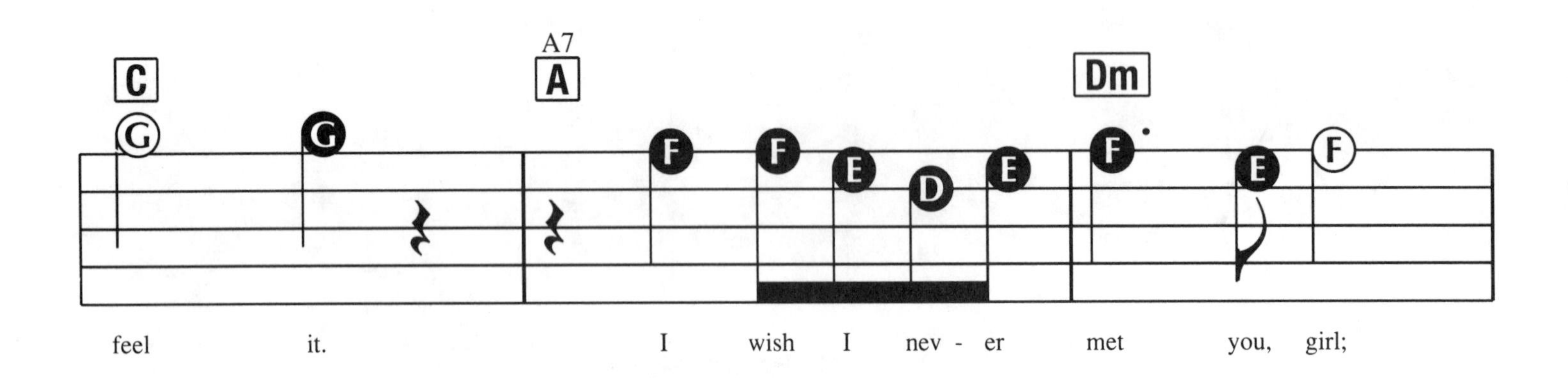
C
G
G
A7
A
F
F
E
D
E
Dm
F
E
F
feel it. I wish I nev - er met you, girl;

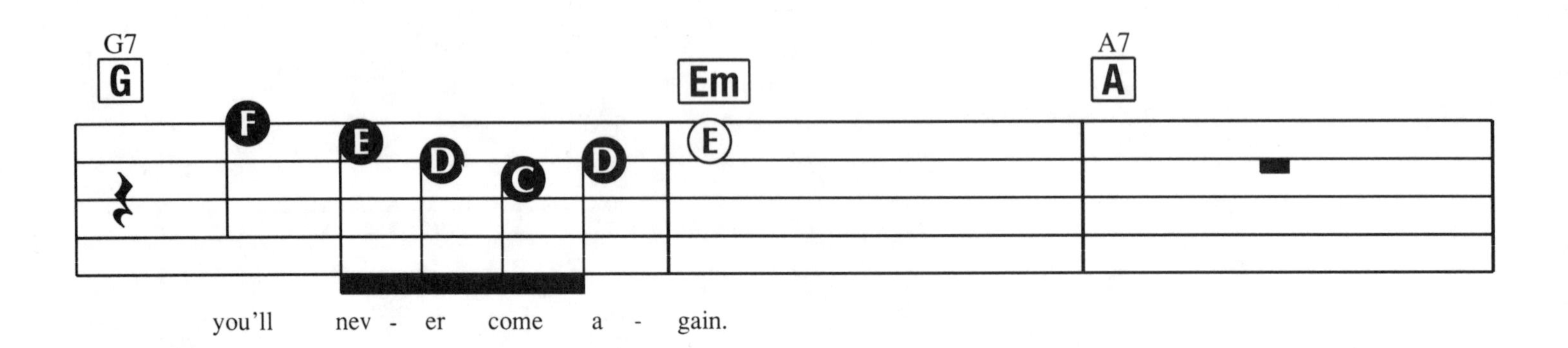
G7
G
F
E
D
C
D
Em
E
A7
A
you'll nev - er come a - gain.

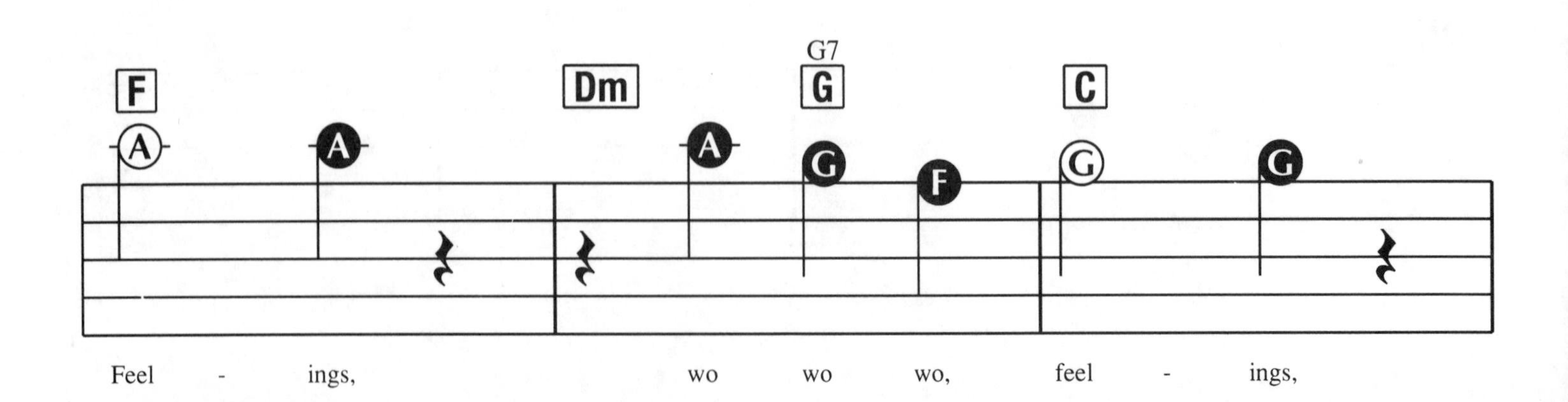
F
A
A
Dm
A
G7
G
G
F
C
G
G
Feel - ings, wo wo wo, feel - ings,

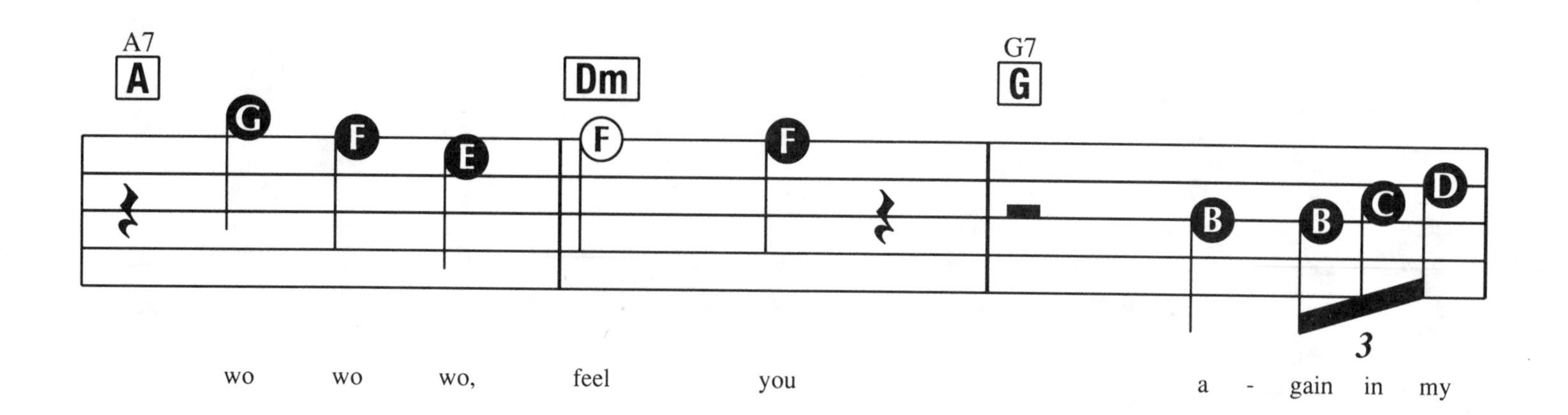
A7
A
Dm
G7
G
G F E F F B B C D
3
wo wo wo, feel you a - gain in my

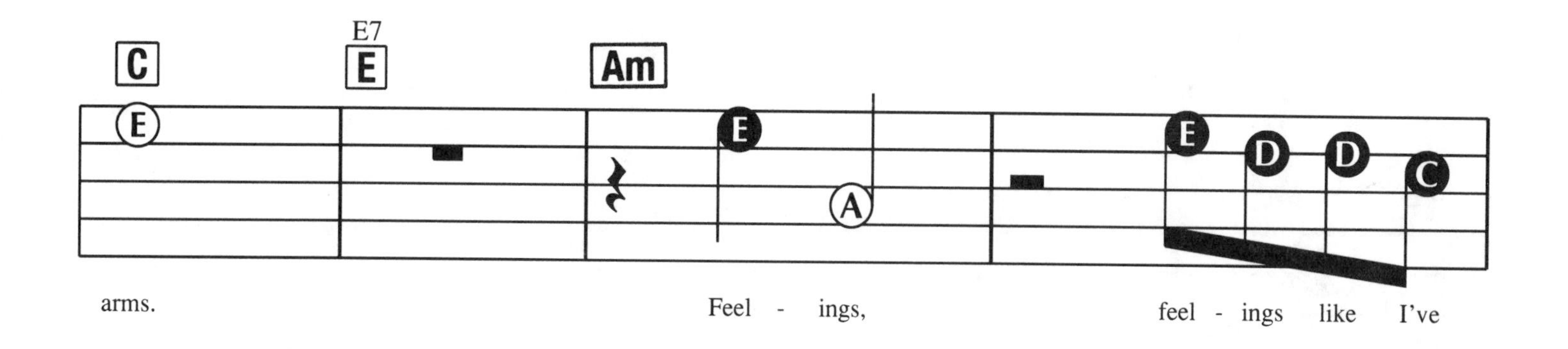
C
E7
E
Am
E E A E D D C
arms. Feel - ings, feel - ings like I've

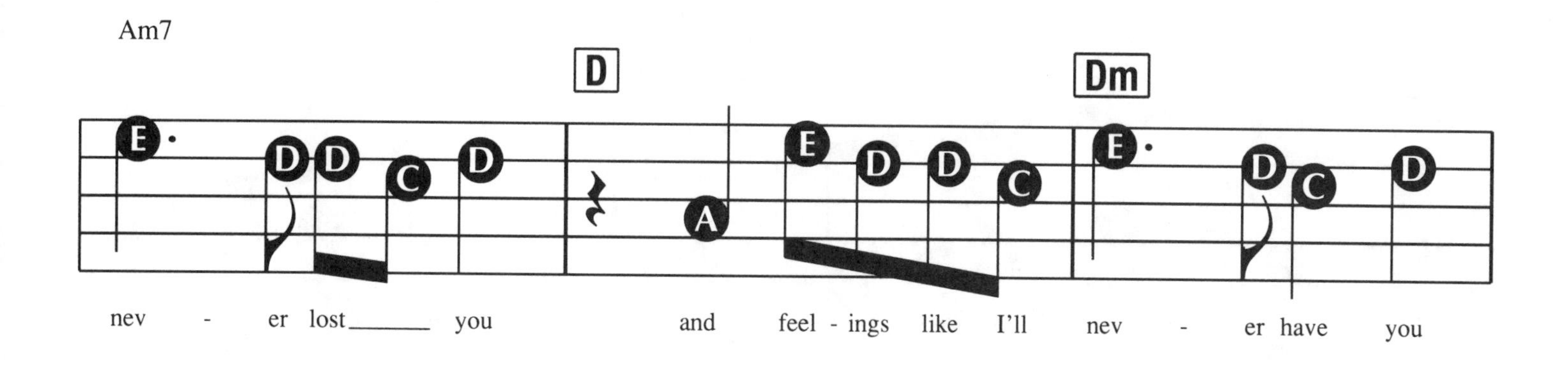
Am7
D
Dm
E D D C D A E D D C E D C D
nev - er lost you and feel - ings like I'll nev - er have you

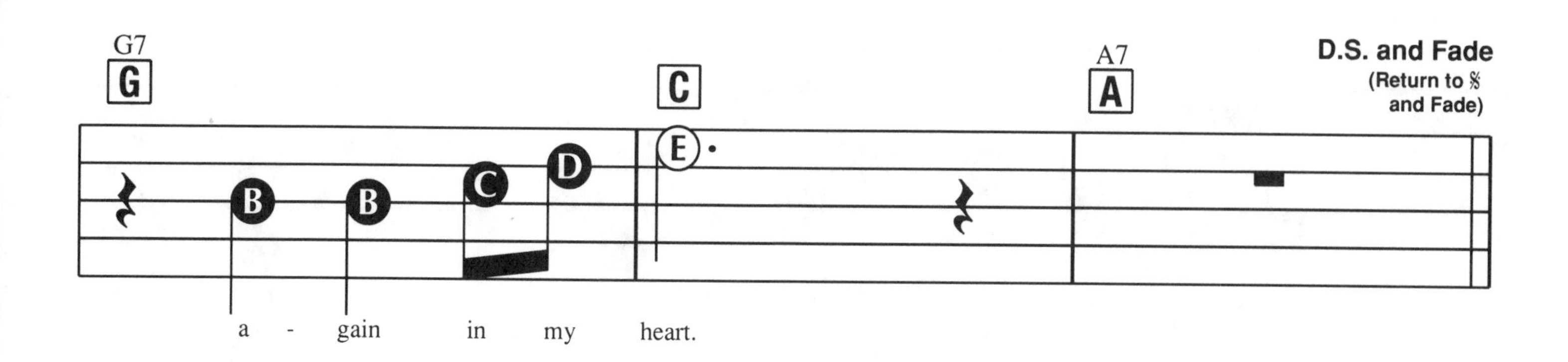
G7
G
C
A7
A
D.S. and Fade
(Return to 𝄋 and Fade)
B B C D E
a - gain in my heart.

Have I Told You Lately

Registration 2
Rhythm: Rock or 8 Beat

Words and Music by
Van Morrison

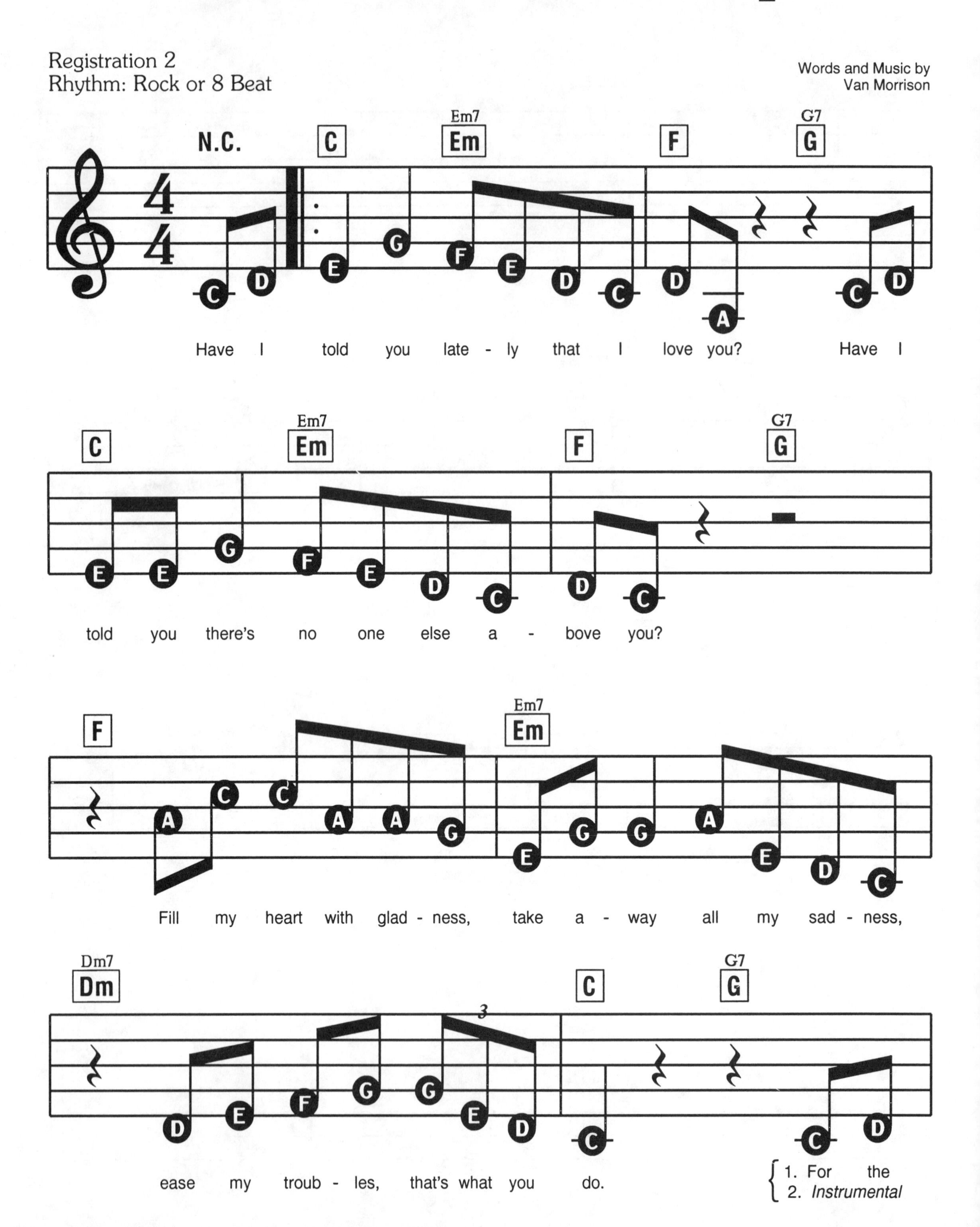

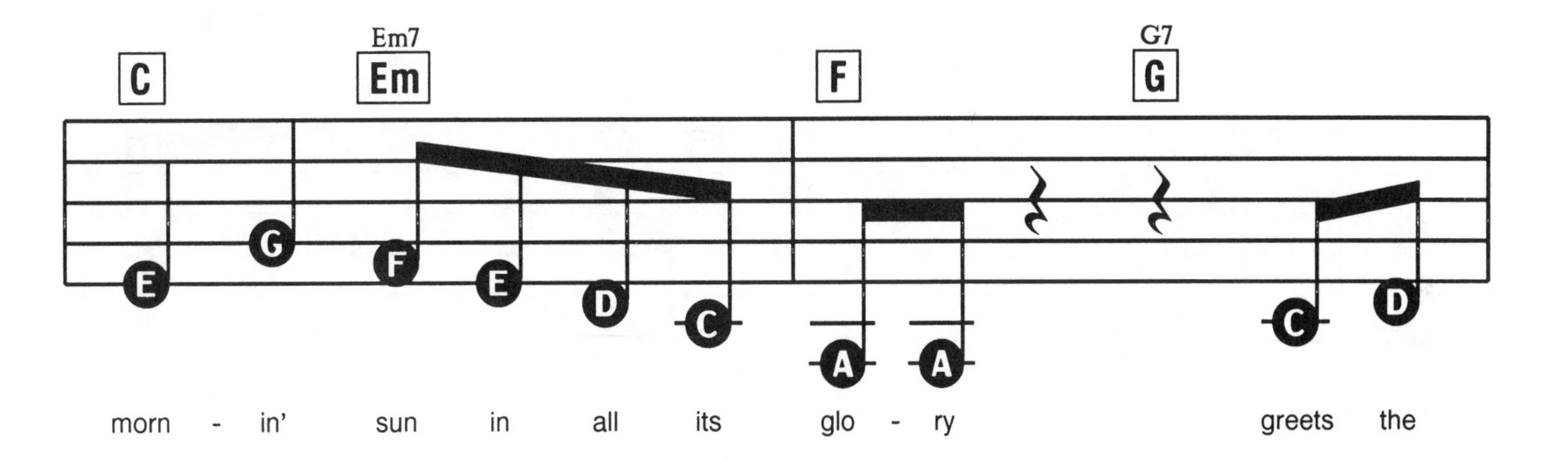
Em7
G7
C
Em
F
G
E
G
F
E
D
C
A
A
C
D
morn - in' sun in all its glo - ry greets the

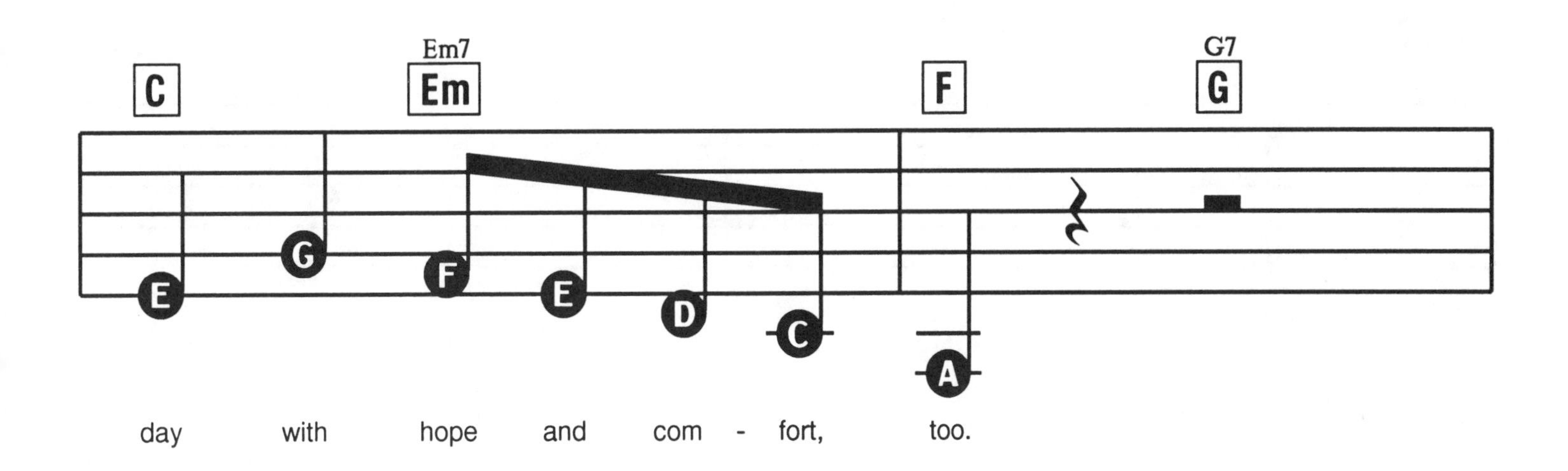
Em7
G7
C
Em
F
G
E
G
F
E
D
C
A
day with hope and com - fort, too.

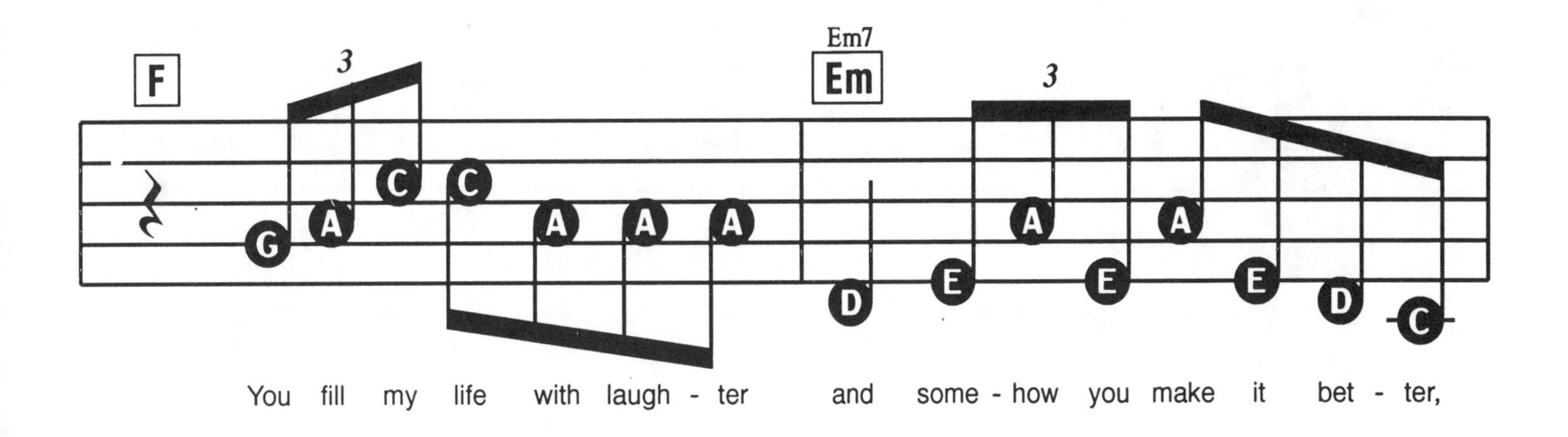
Em7
F
Em
3
3
G
A
C
C
A
A
A
D
E
A
E
A
E
D
C
You fill my life with laugh - ter and some - how you make it bet - ter,

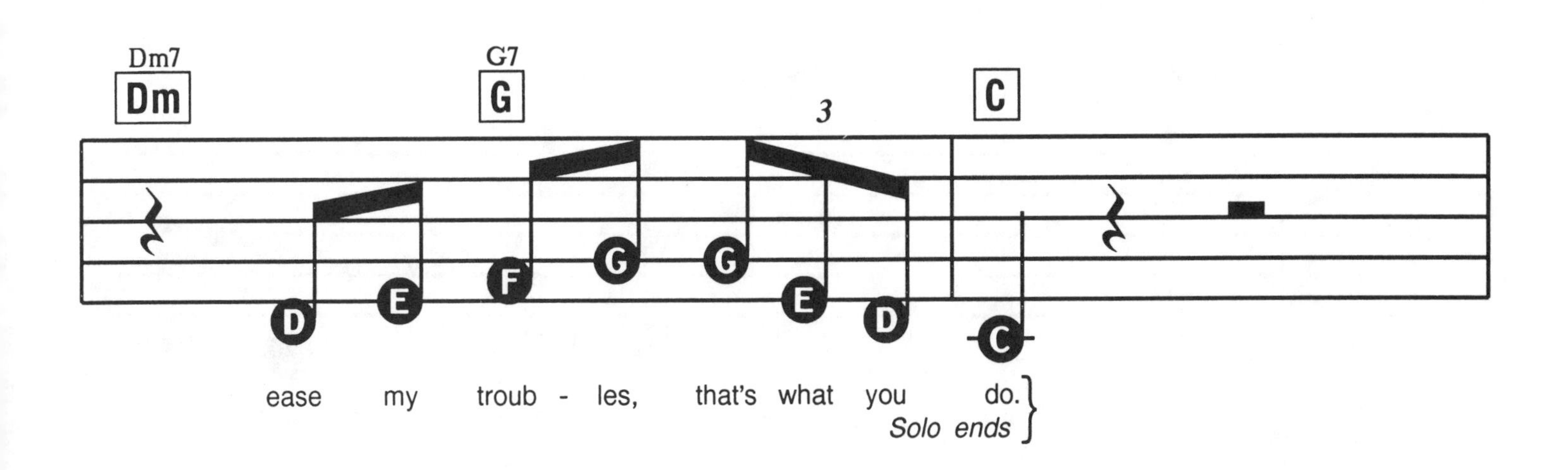
Dm7
G7
Dm
G
C
3
D
E
F
G
G
E
D
C
ease my troub - les, that's what you do.
Solo ends

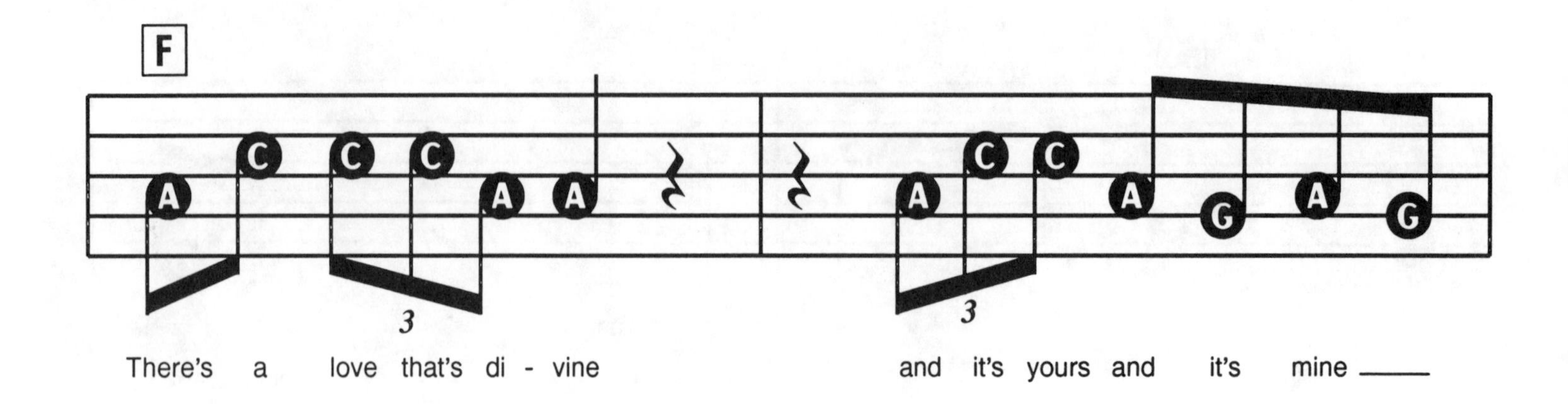
F
A
C
C
C
A
A
3
A
C
C
A
G
A
G
3
There's a love that's di - vine
and it's yours and it's mine

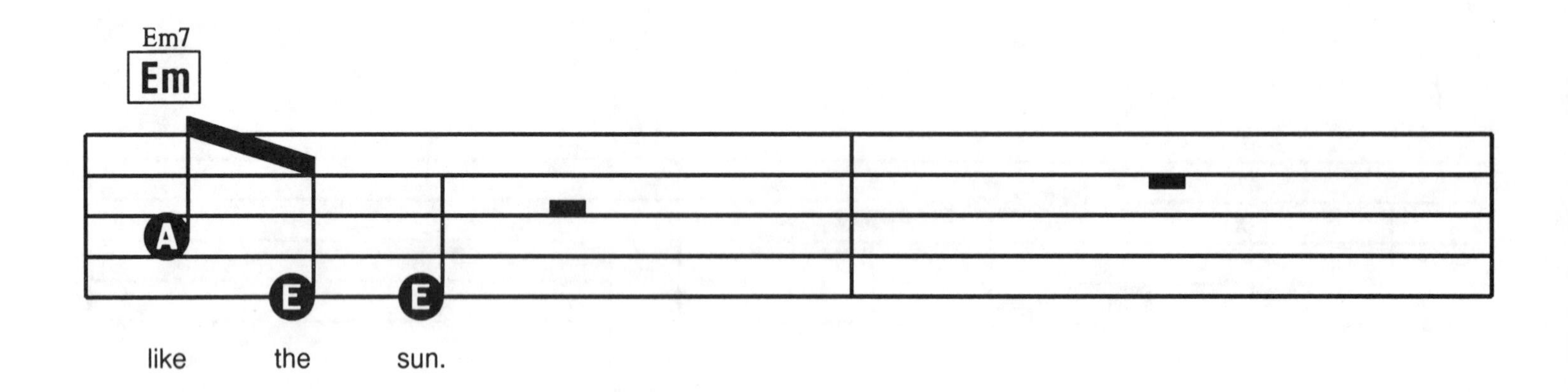
Em7
Em
A
E
E
like the sun.

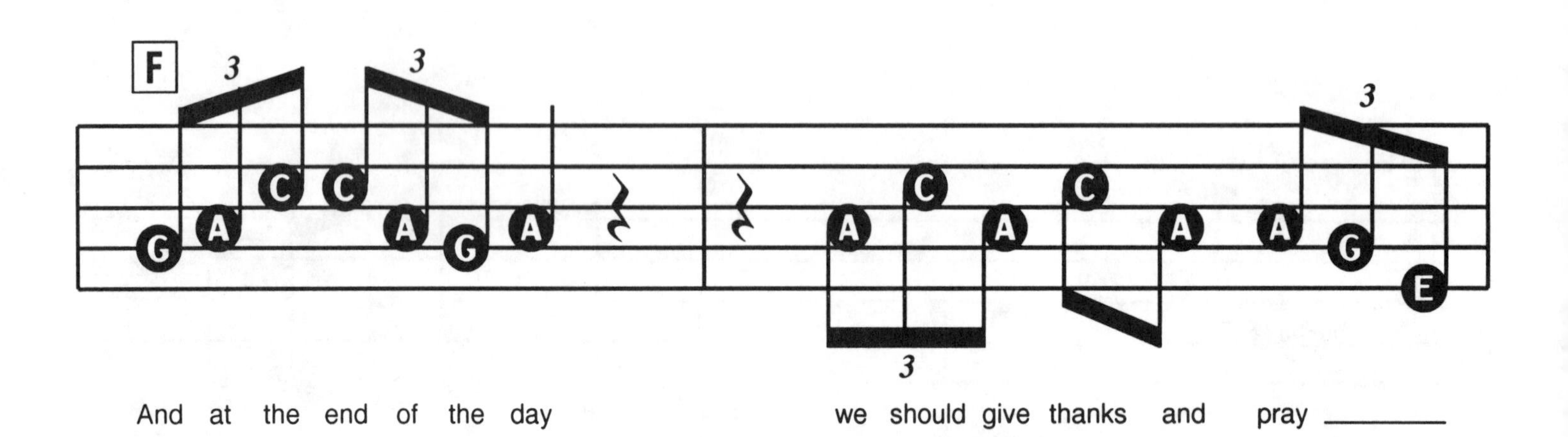
F
3
3
G
A
C
C
A
G
A
A
C
A
C
A
A
G
E
3
3
And at the end of the day
we should give thanks and pray

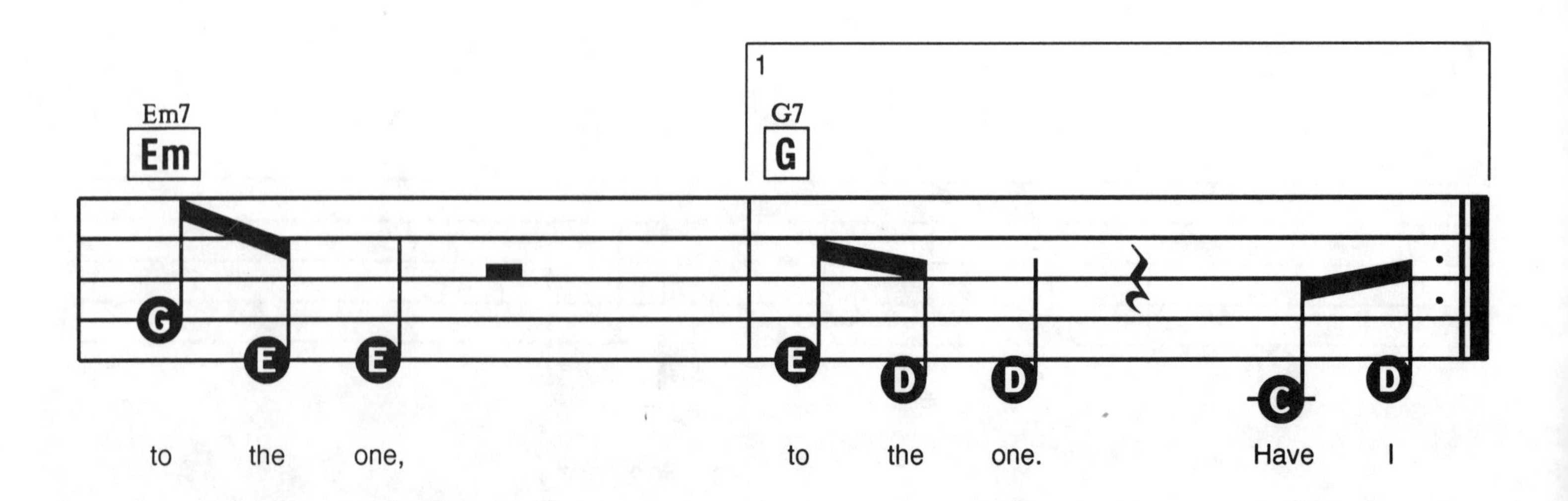
1
Em7
Em
G7
G
G
E
E
E
D
D
C
D
to the one,
to the one.
Have I

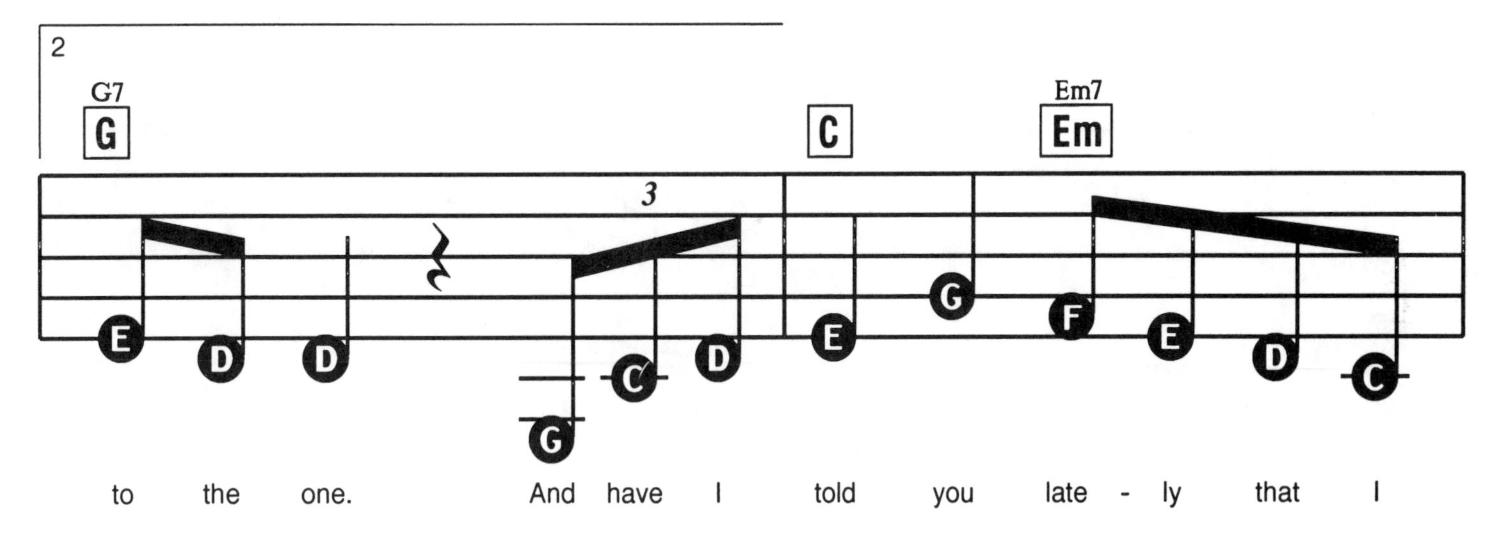
2
G7
G
C
Em7
Em
3
E D D G C D E G F E D C
to the one. And have I told you late - ly that I

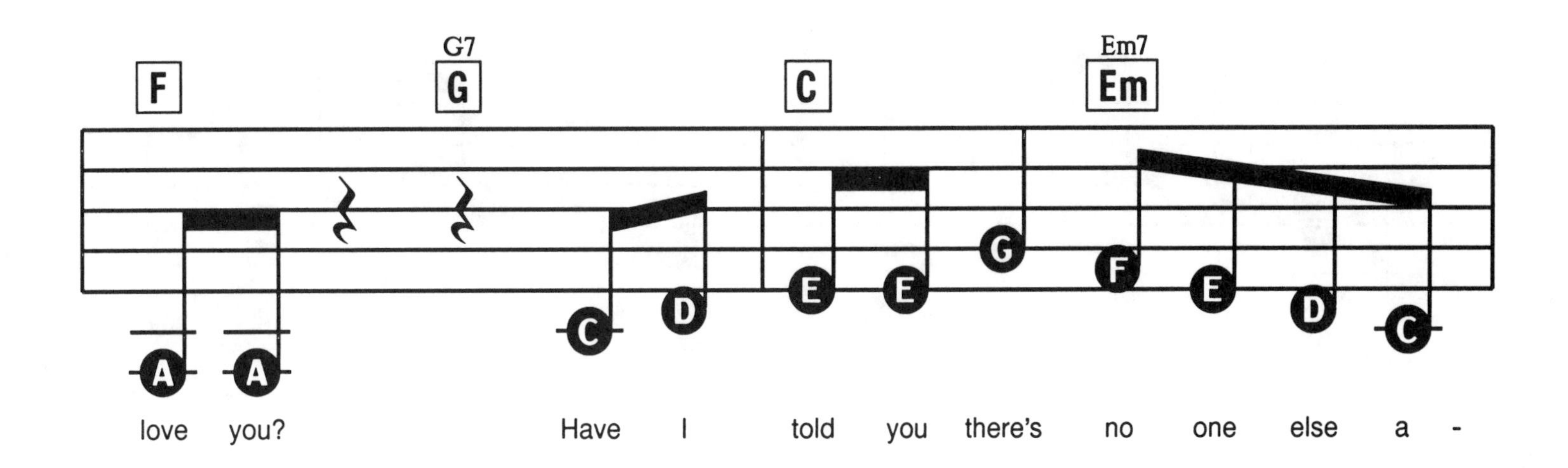
F
G7
G
C
Em7
Em
A A C D E E G F E D C
love you? Have I told you there's no one else a -

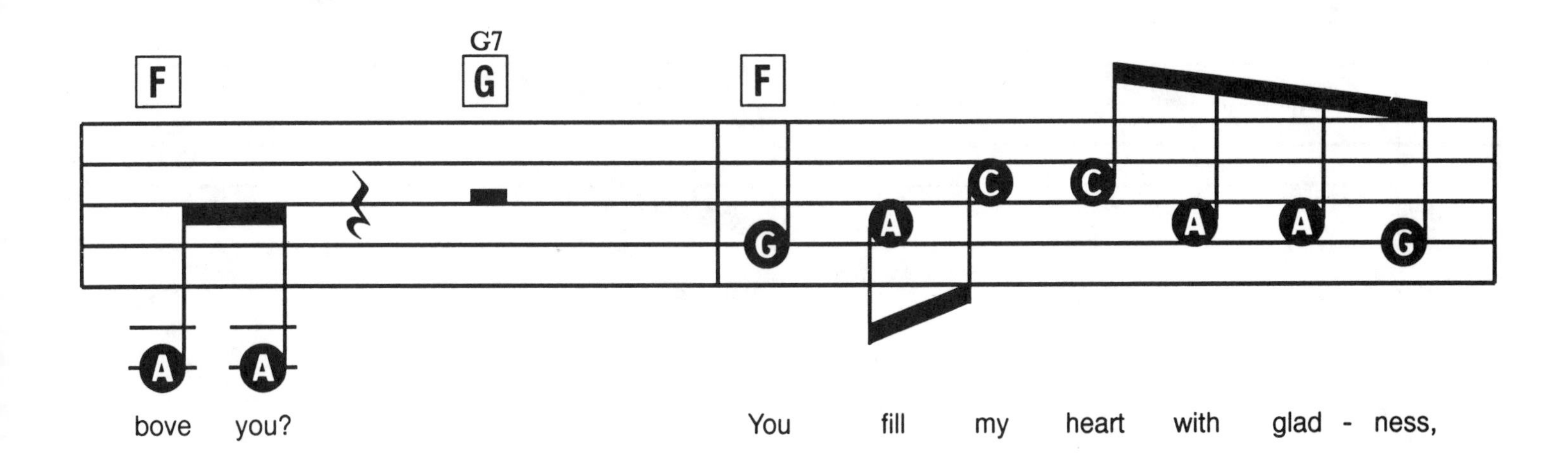
F
G7
G
F
A A G A C C A A G
bove you? You fill my heart with glad - ness,

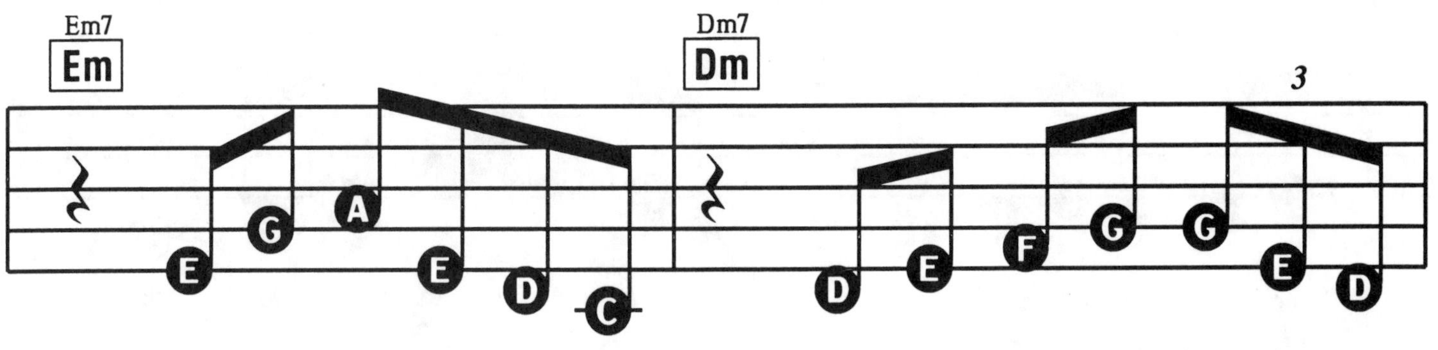
Em7
Em
Dm7
Dm
3
E G A E D C D E F G G E D
take a - way my sad - ness, ease my troub - les, that's what you

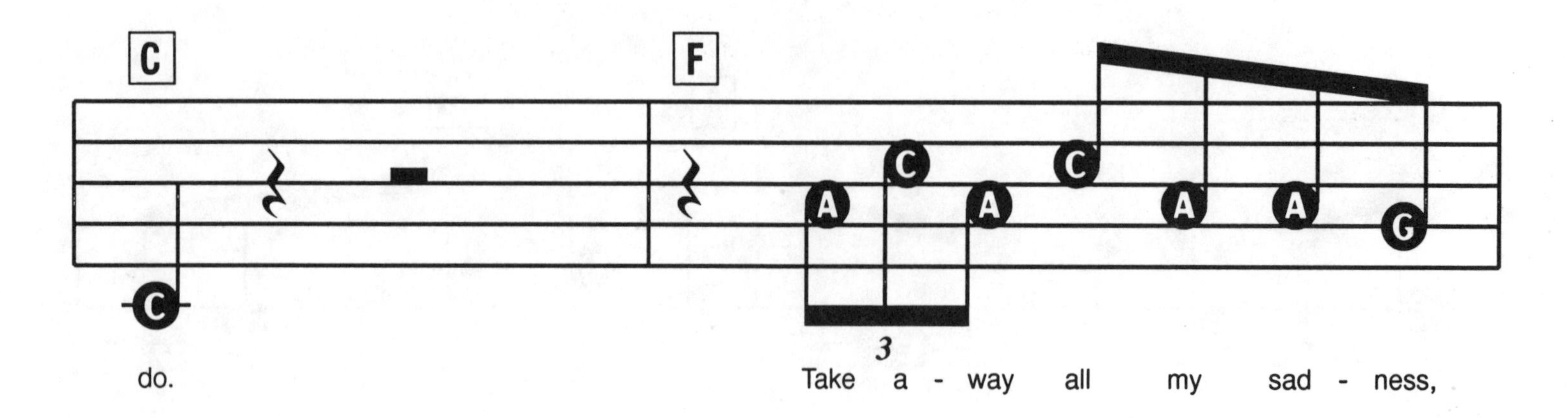
C
F
C
A C A C A A G
3
do.
Take a - way all my sad - ness,

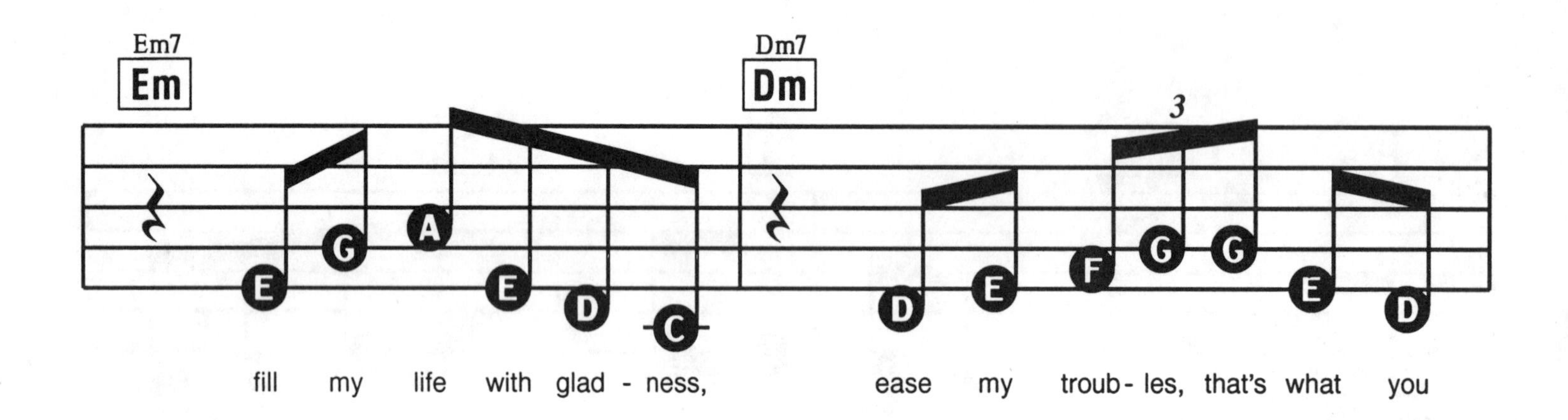
Em7
Em
Dm7
Dm
E G A E D C
D E F G G E D
3
fill my life with glad - ness,
ease my troub - les, that's what you

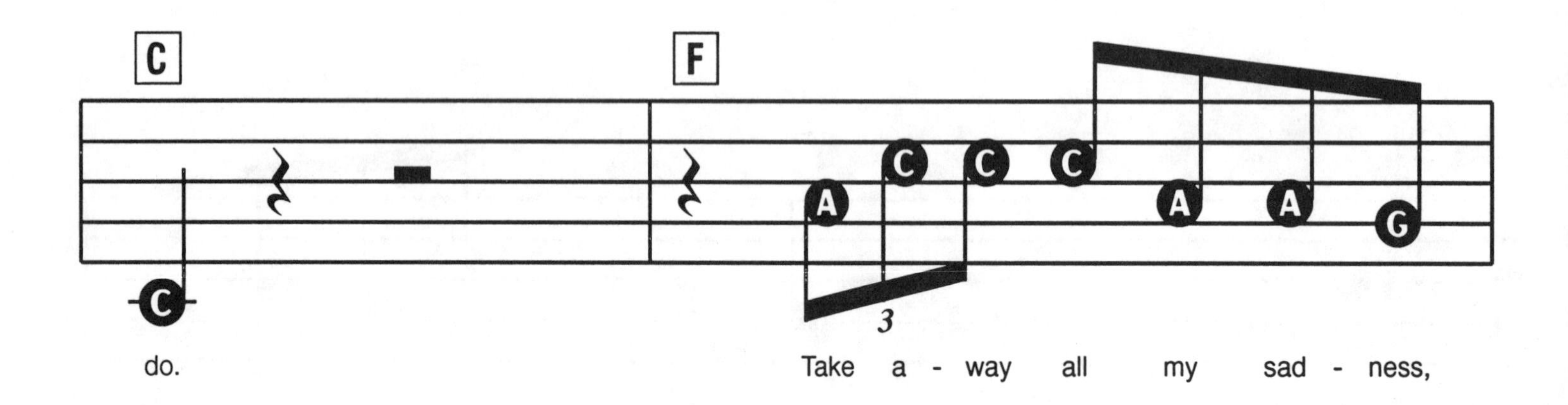
C
F
C
A C C C A A G
3
do.
Take a - way all my sad - ness,

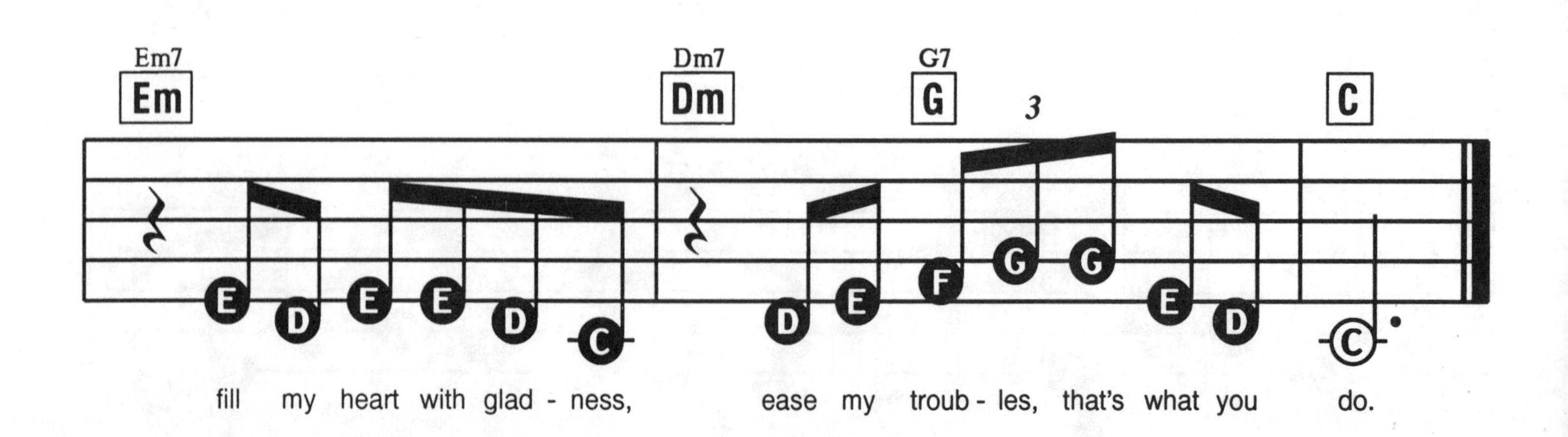
Em7
Em
Dm7
Dm
G7
G
C
E D E E D C
D E F G G E D
C
3
fill my heart with glad - ness,
ease my troub - les, that's what you
do.

Sunrise, Sunset

from the Musical FIDDLER ON THE ROOF

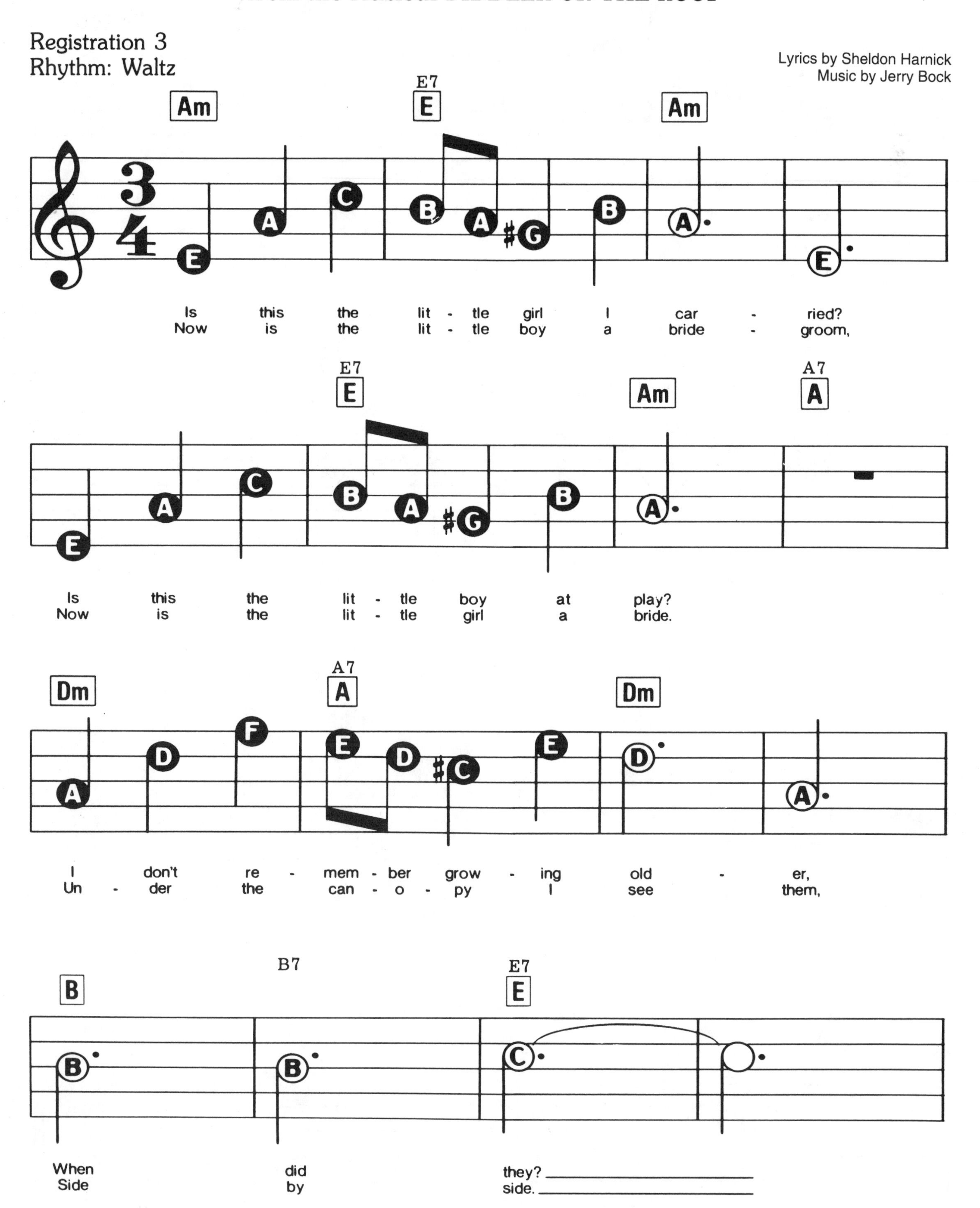

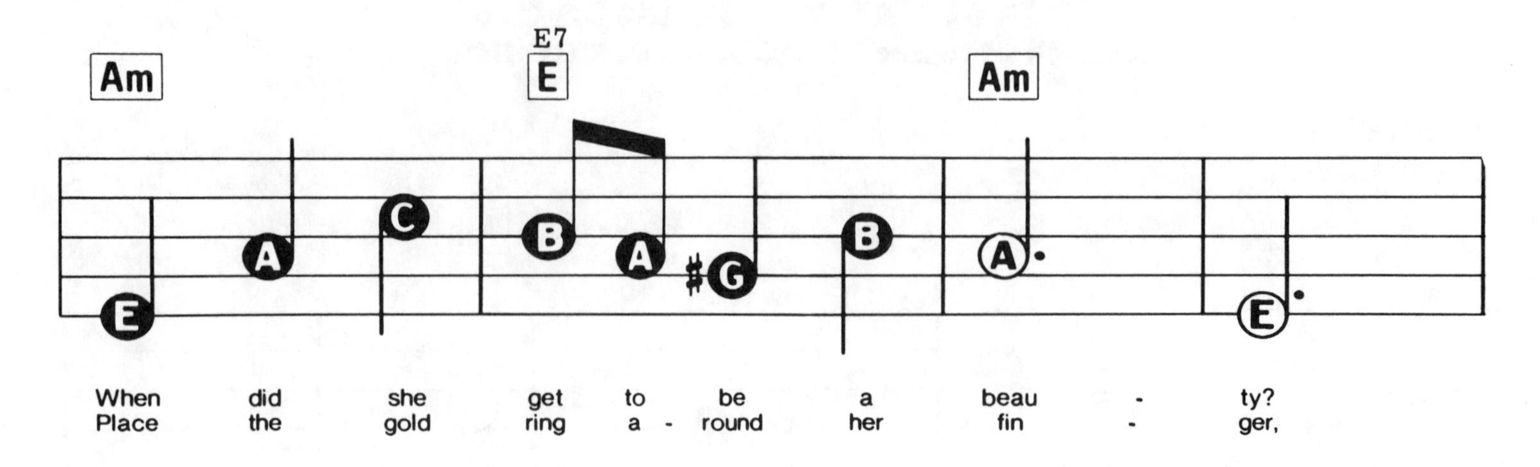
Am
E7
E
Am
E A C B A #G B A E
When did she get to be a beau - ty?
Place the gold ring a - round her fin - ger,

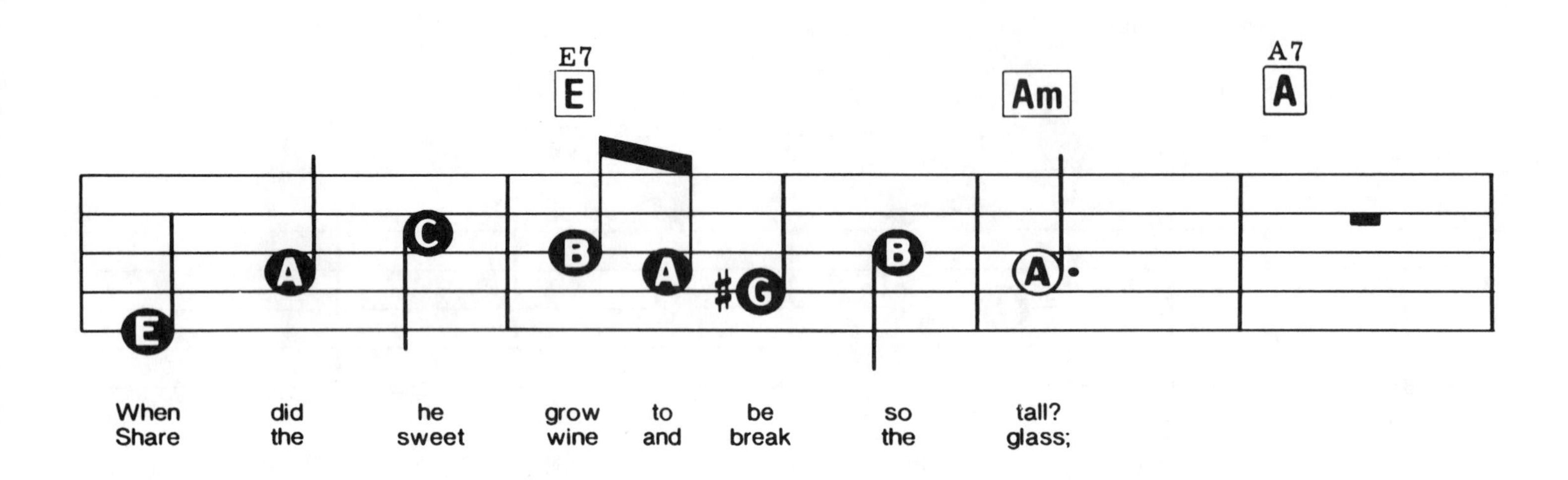
E7
E
Am
A7
A
E A C B A #G B A
When did he grow to be so tall?
Share the sweet wine and break the glass;

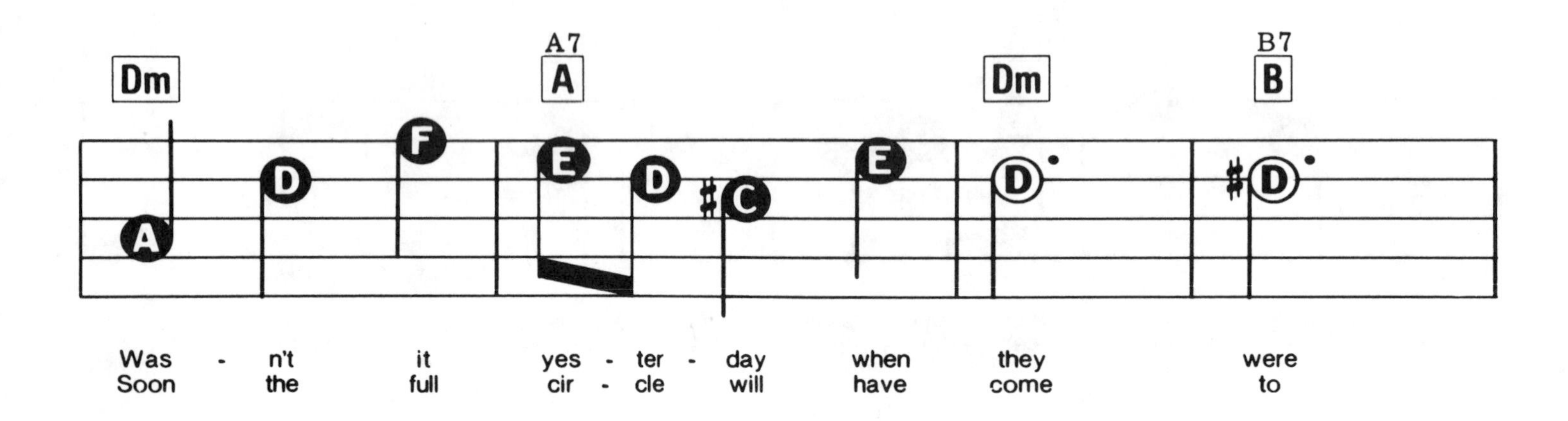
Dm
A7
A
Dm
B7
B
A D F E D #C E D #D
Was - n't it yes - ter - day when they were
Soon the full cir - cle will have come to

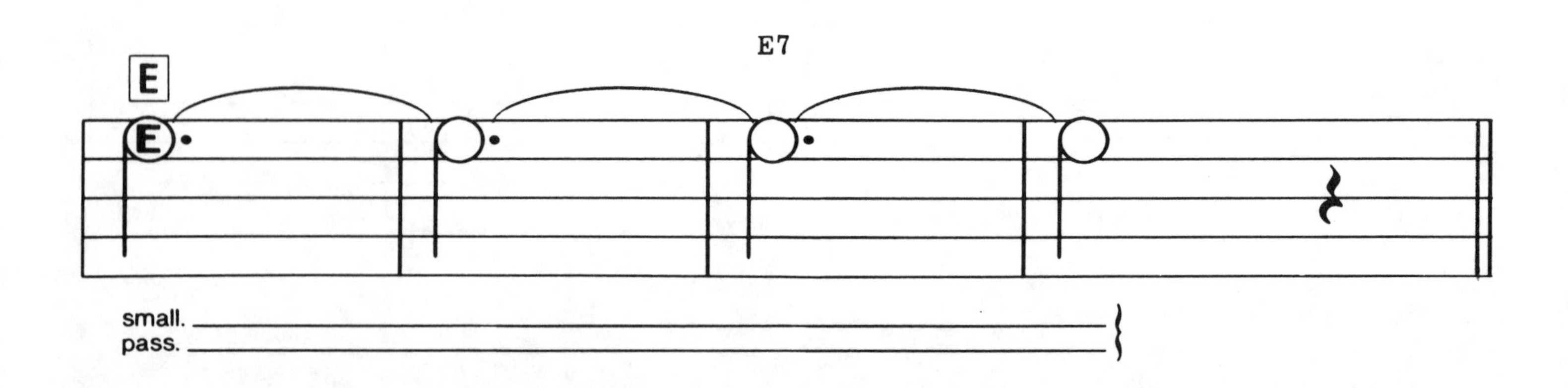
E
E7
E
small.
pass.

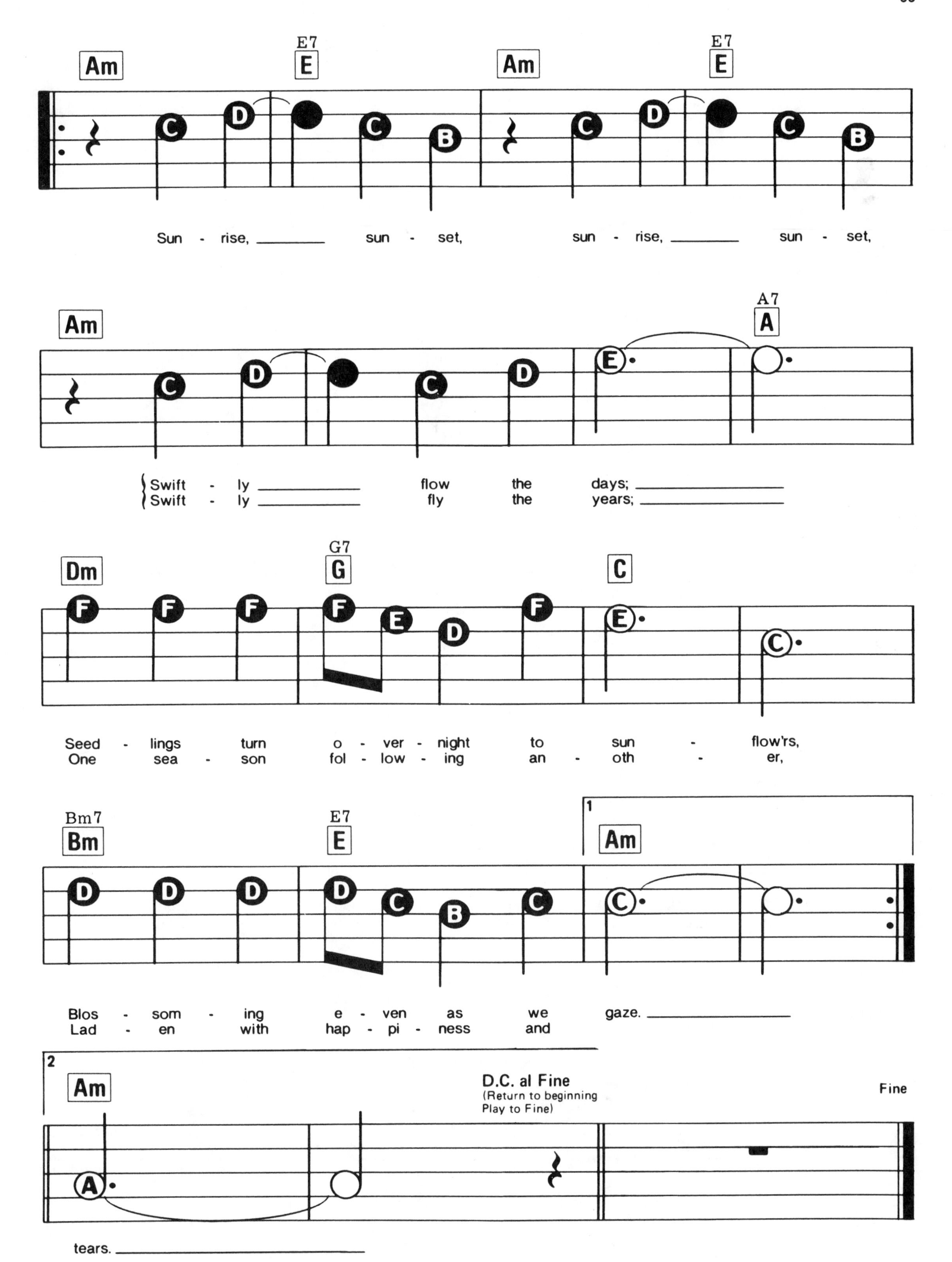

Am
E7
E
Am
E7
E
C D C B C D C B
Sun - rise, sun - set, sun - rise, sun - set,
Am
A7
A
C D C D E
Swift - ly flow the days;
Swift - ly fly the years;
Dm
G7
G
C
F F F F E D F E C
Seed - lings turn o - ver - night to sun - flow'rs,
One sea - son fol - low - ing an - oth - er,
Bm7
Bm
E7
E
1
Am
D D D D C B C C
Blos - som - ing e - ven as we gaze.
Lad - en with hap - pi - ness and
2
Am
A
D.C. al Fine
(Return to beginning
Play to Fine)
Fine
tears.

Isn't It Romantic?

from the Paramount Picture LOVE ME TONIGHT

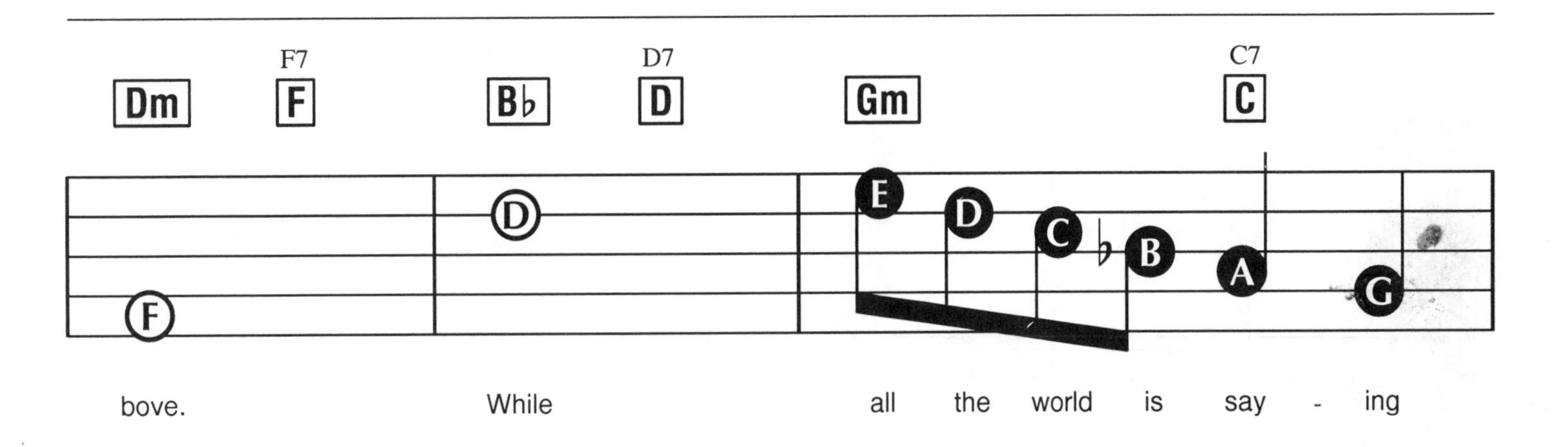
F7
Dm
F
Bb
D7
D
Gm
C7
C
F
D
E
D
C
B
A
G
bove.
While
all the world is say - ing

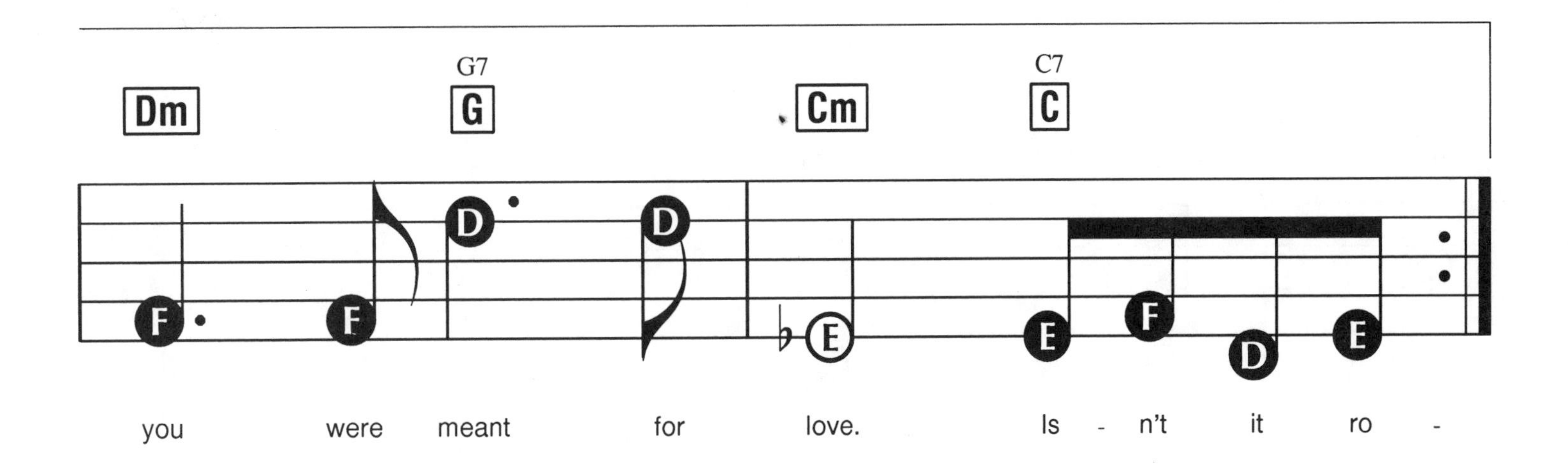
G7
Dm
G
Cm
C7
C
F
F
D
D
E
E
F
D
E
you were meant for love.
Is - n't it ro -

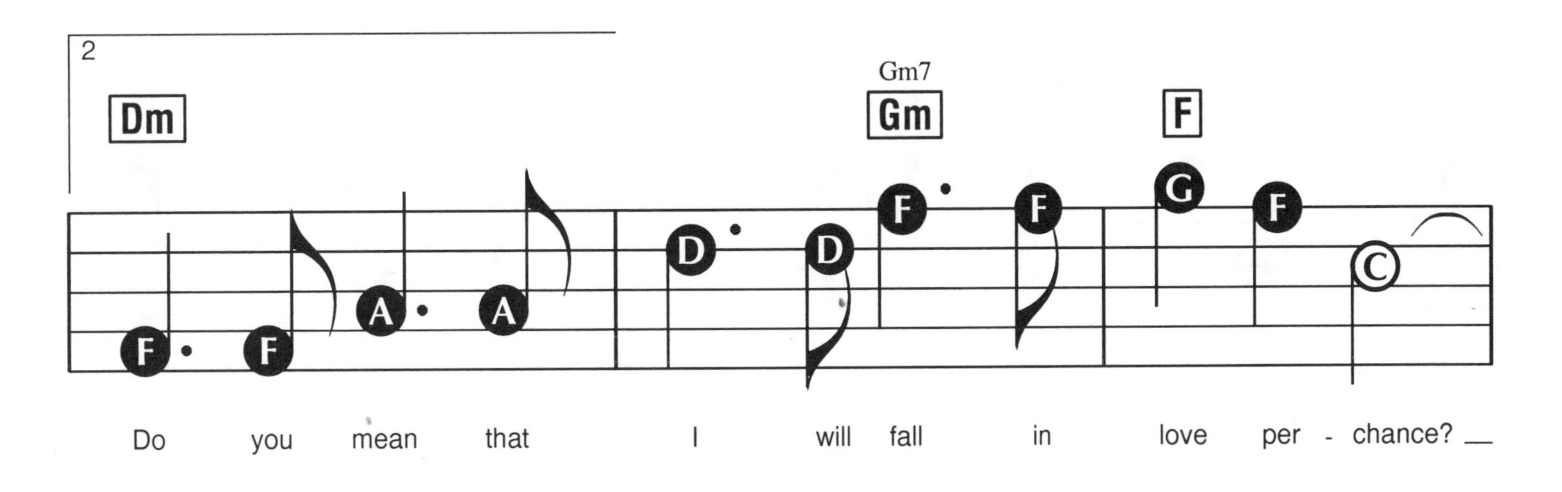
2
Dm
Gm7
Gm
F
F
F
A
A
D
D
F
F
G
F
C
Do you mean that I will fall in love per - chance?

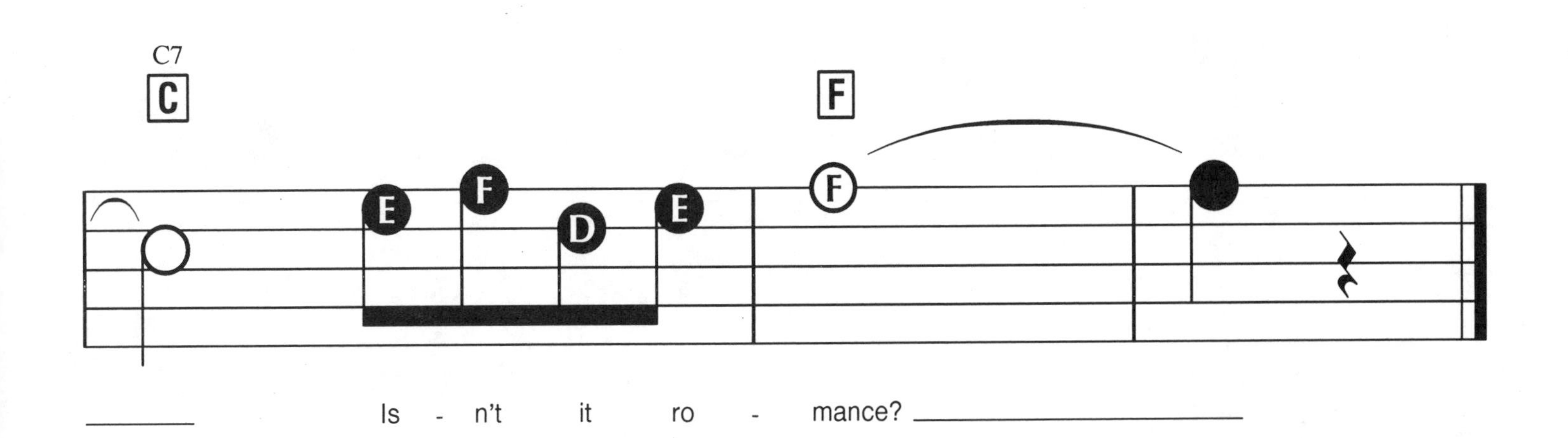
C7
C
F
E
F
D
E
F
Is - n't it ro - mance?

Love Me Tender

Registration 9
Rhythm: Fox Trot

Words and Music by Elvis Presley
and Vera Matson

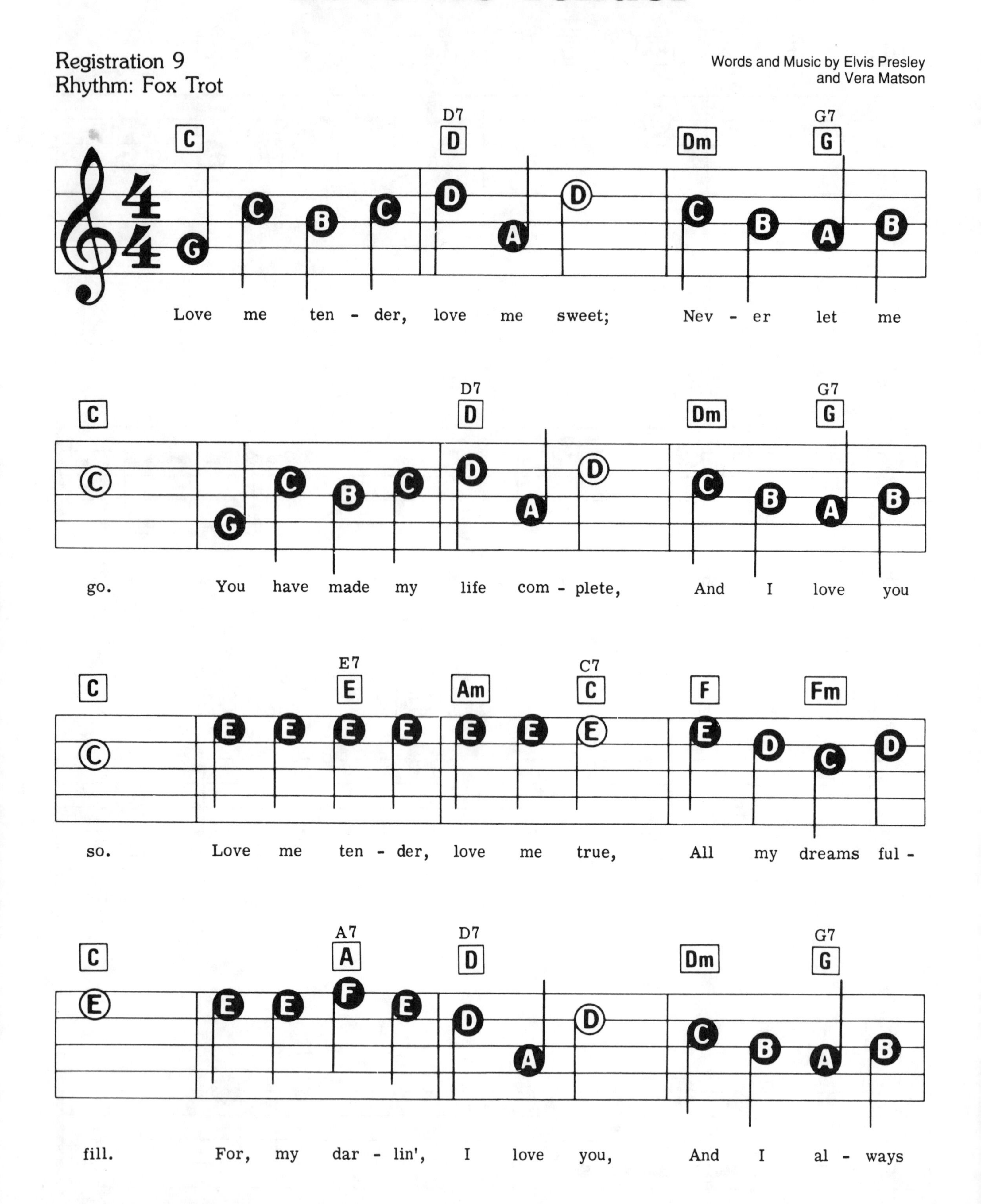

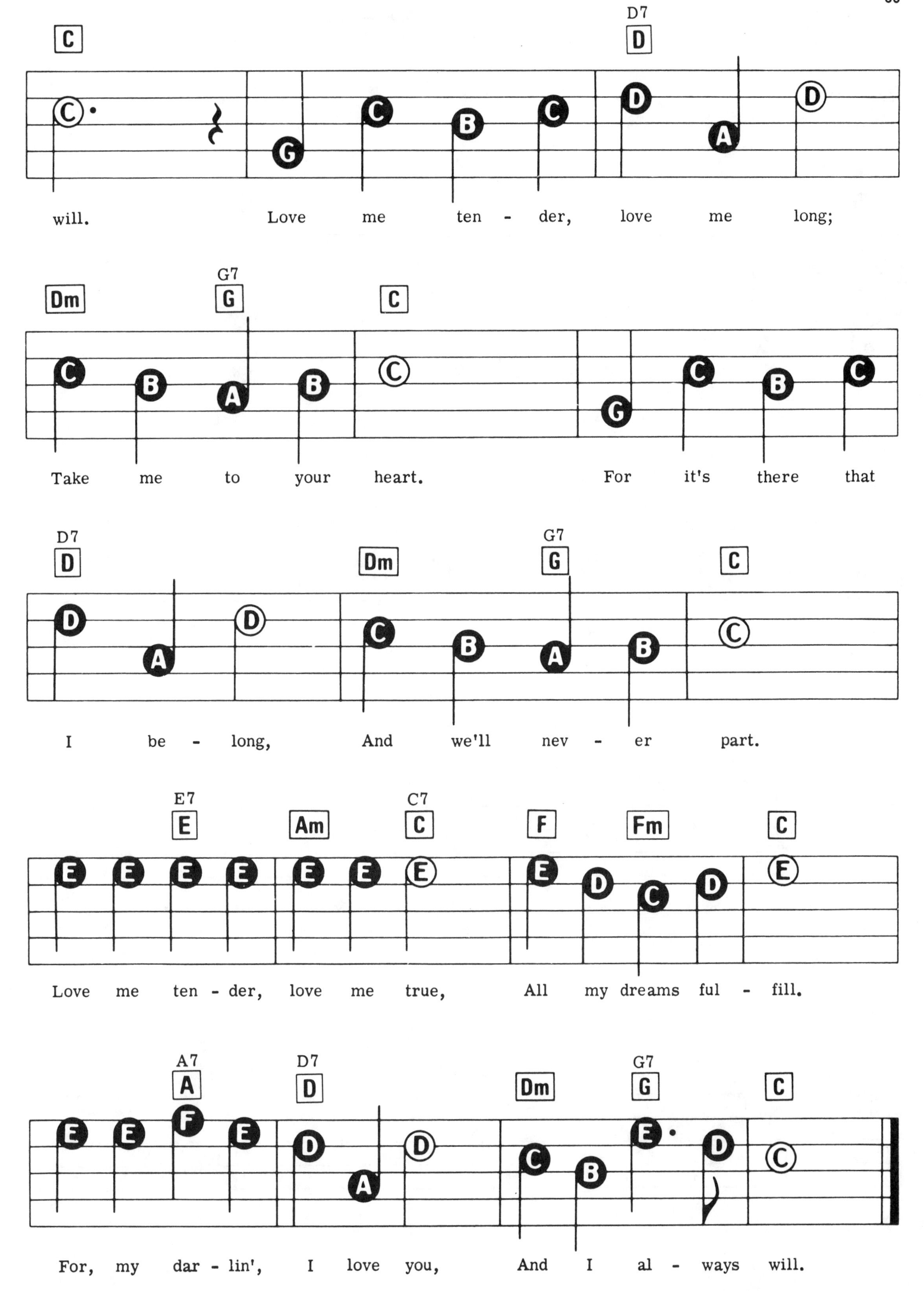
C D7 D
will. Love me ten - der, love me long;
Dm G7 G C
Take me to your heart. For it's there that
D7 D Dm G7 G C
I be - long, And we'll nev - er part.
E7 E Am C7 C F Fm C
Love me ten - der, love me true, All my dreams ful - fill.
A7 A D7 D Dm G7 G C
For, my dar - lin', I love you, And I al - ways will.

Loving You

Registration 4
Rhythm: Ballad or Fox Trot

Words and Music by Jerry Leiber
and Mike Stoller

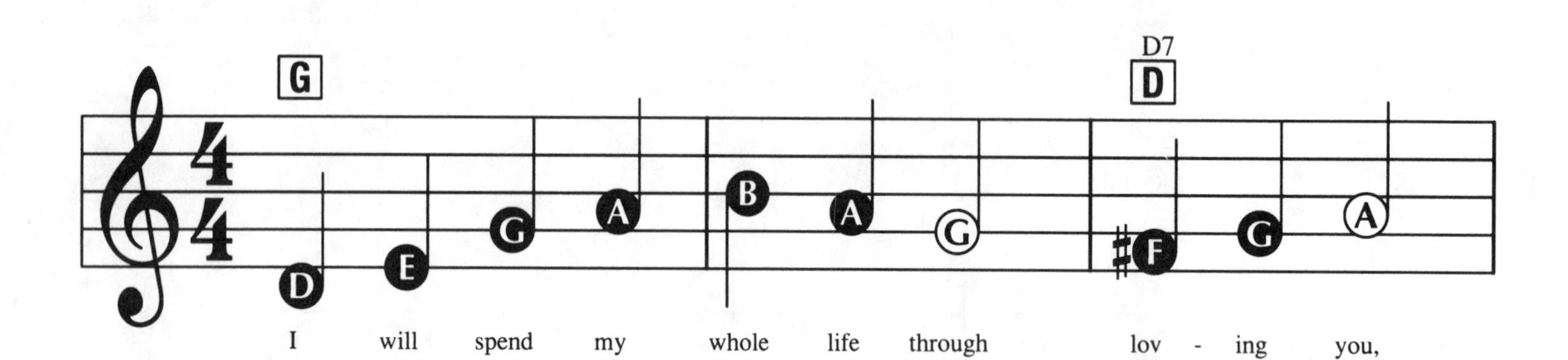

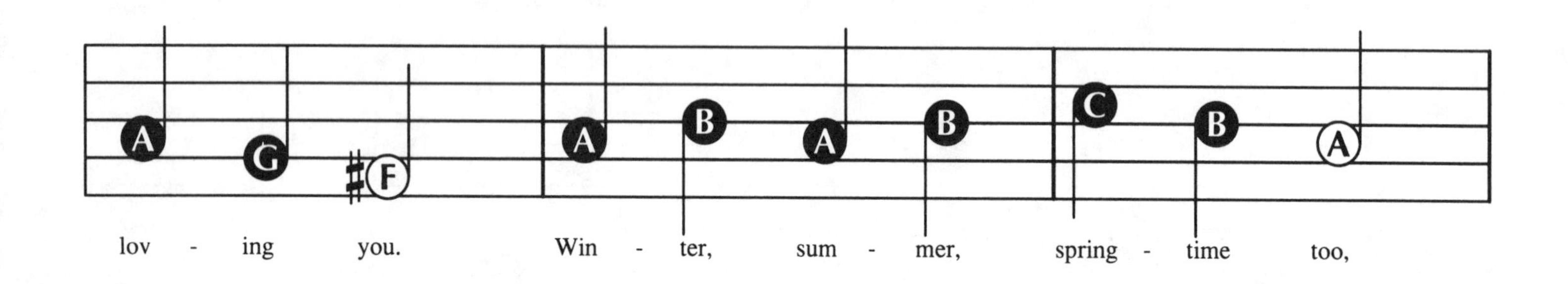

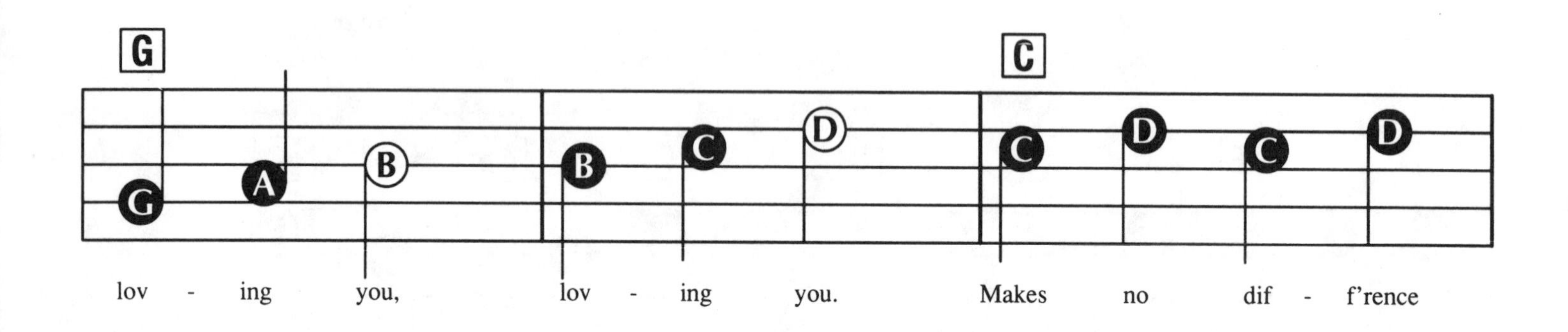

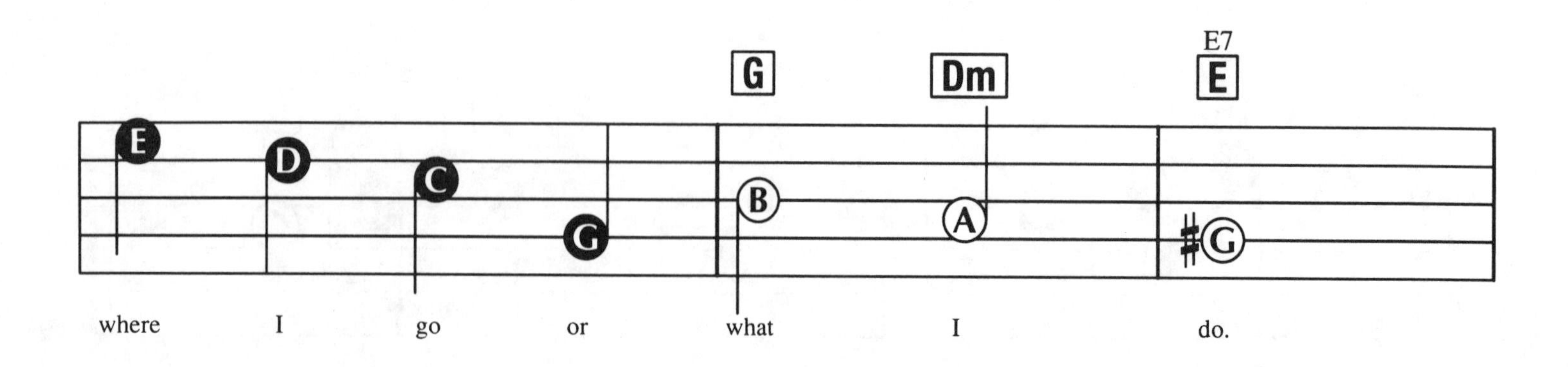

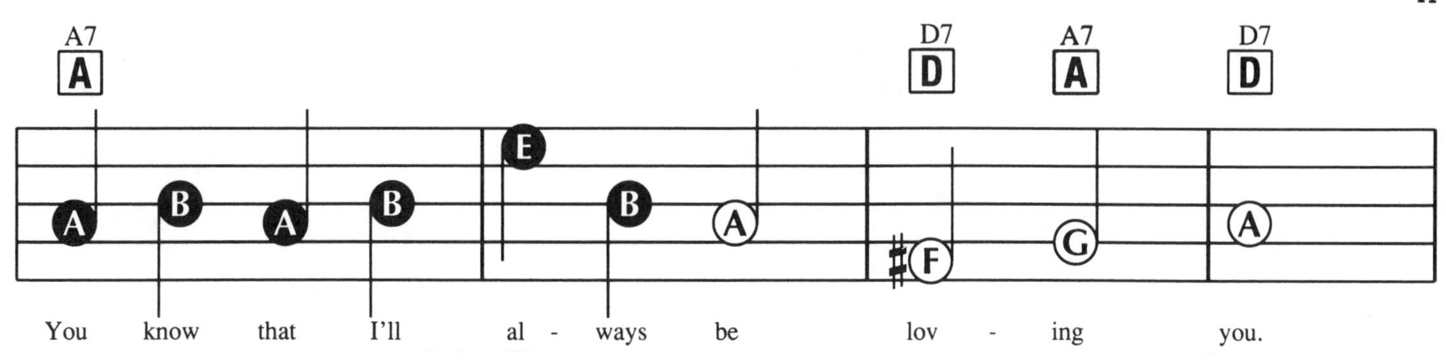
A7 A
D7 D
A7 A
D7 D
A B A B E B A ♯F G A
You know that I'll al - ways be lov - ing you.

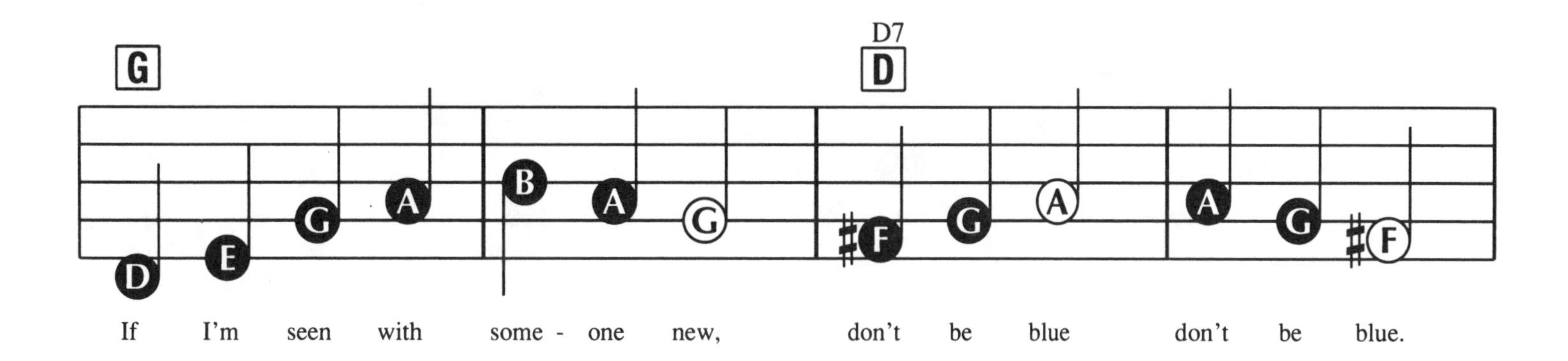
G
D7 D
D E G A B A G ♯F G A A G ♯F
If I'm seen with some - one new, don't be blue don't be blue.

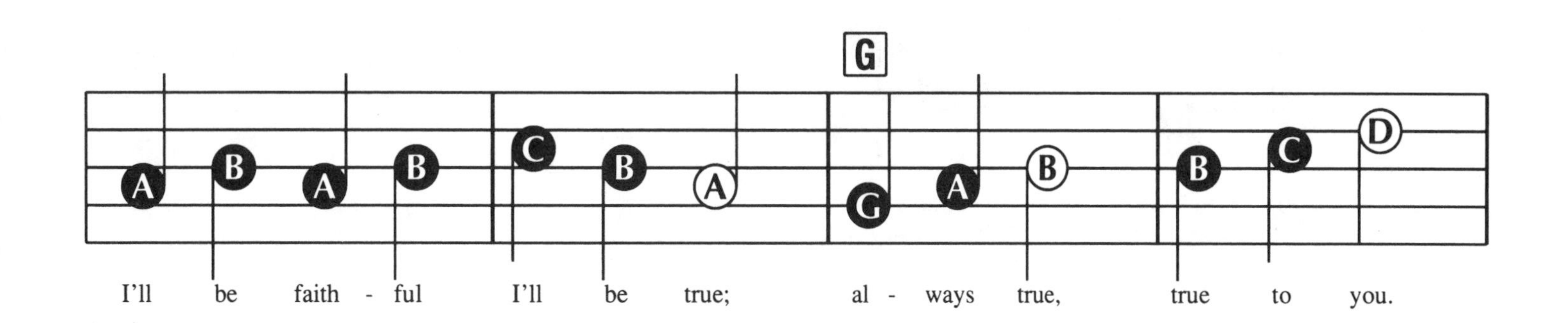
G
A B A B C B A G A B B C D
I'll be faith - ful I'll be true; al - ways true, true to you.

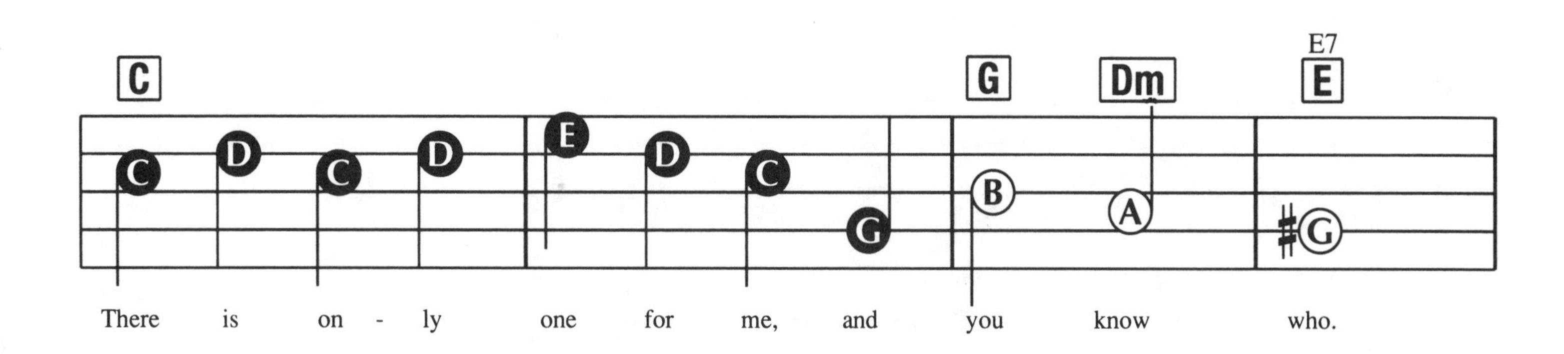
C
G
Dm
E7 E
C D C D E D C G B A ♯G
There is on - ly one for me, and you know who.

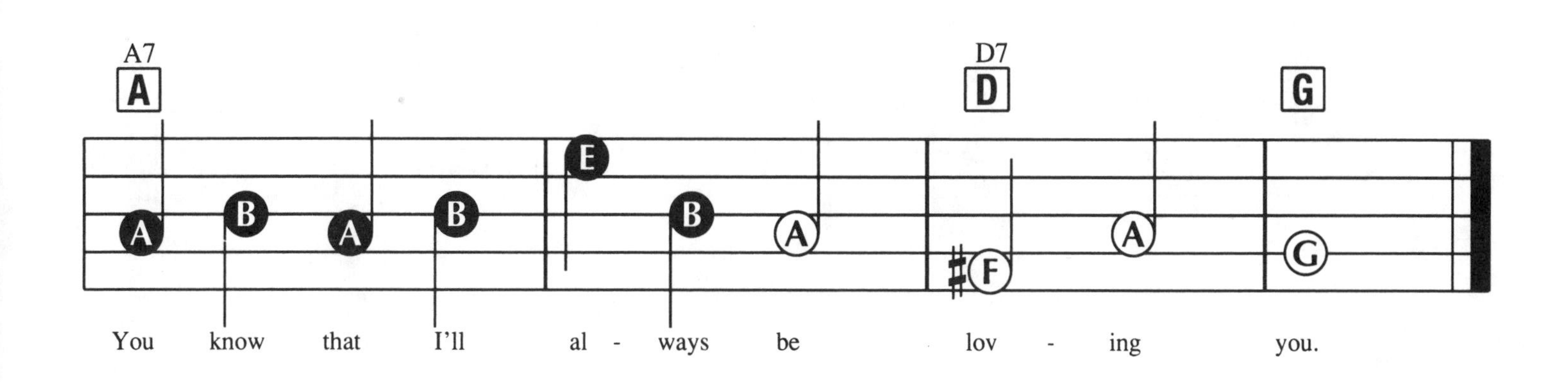
A7 A
D7 D
G
A B A B E B A ♯F A G
You know that I'll al - ways be lov - ing you.

Some Enchanted Evening
from SOUTH PACIFIC

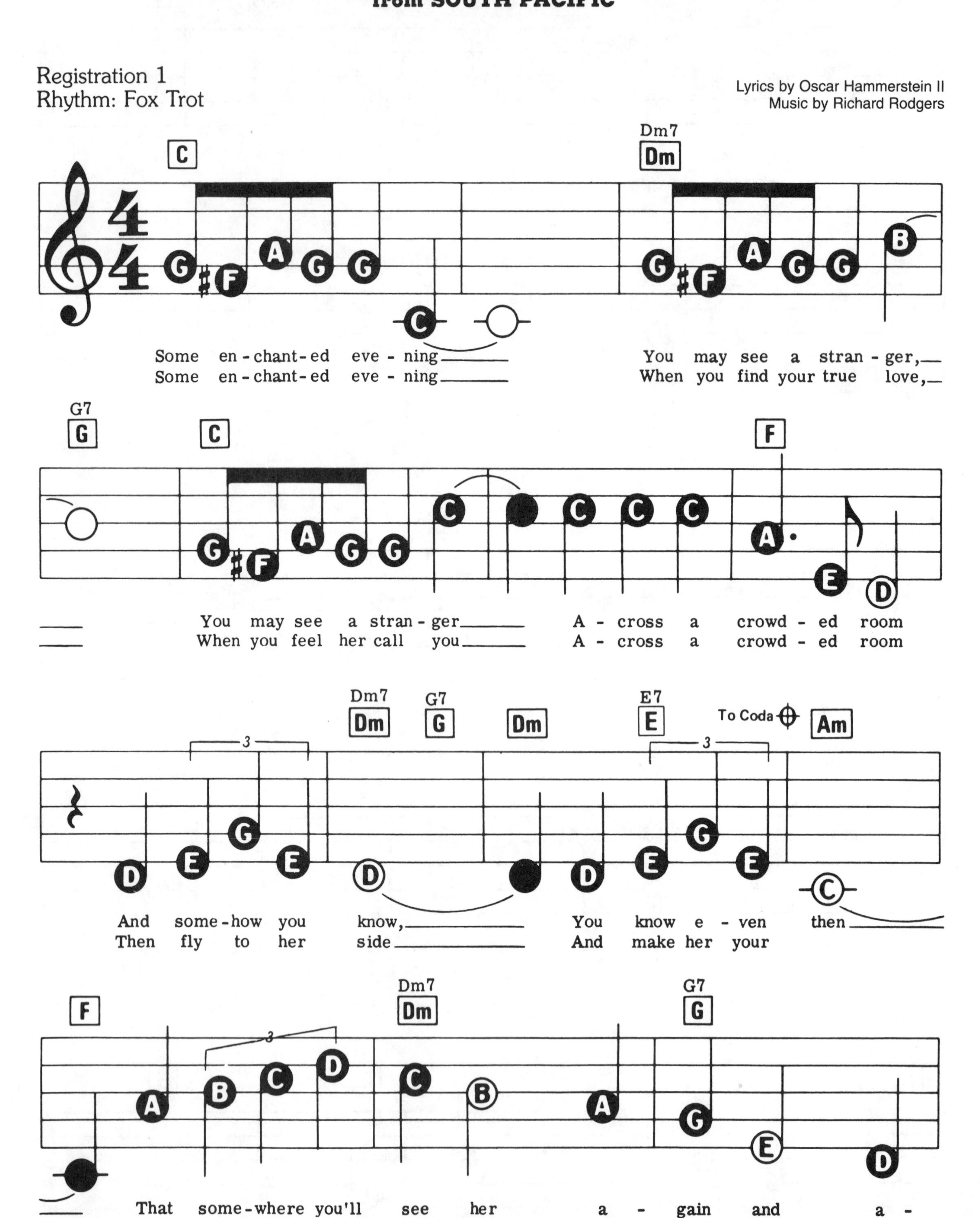

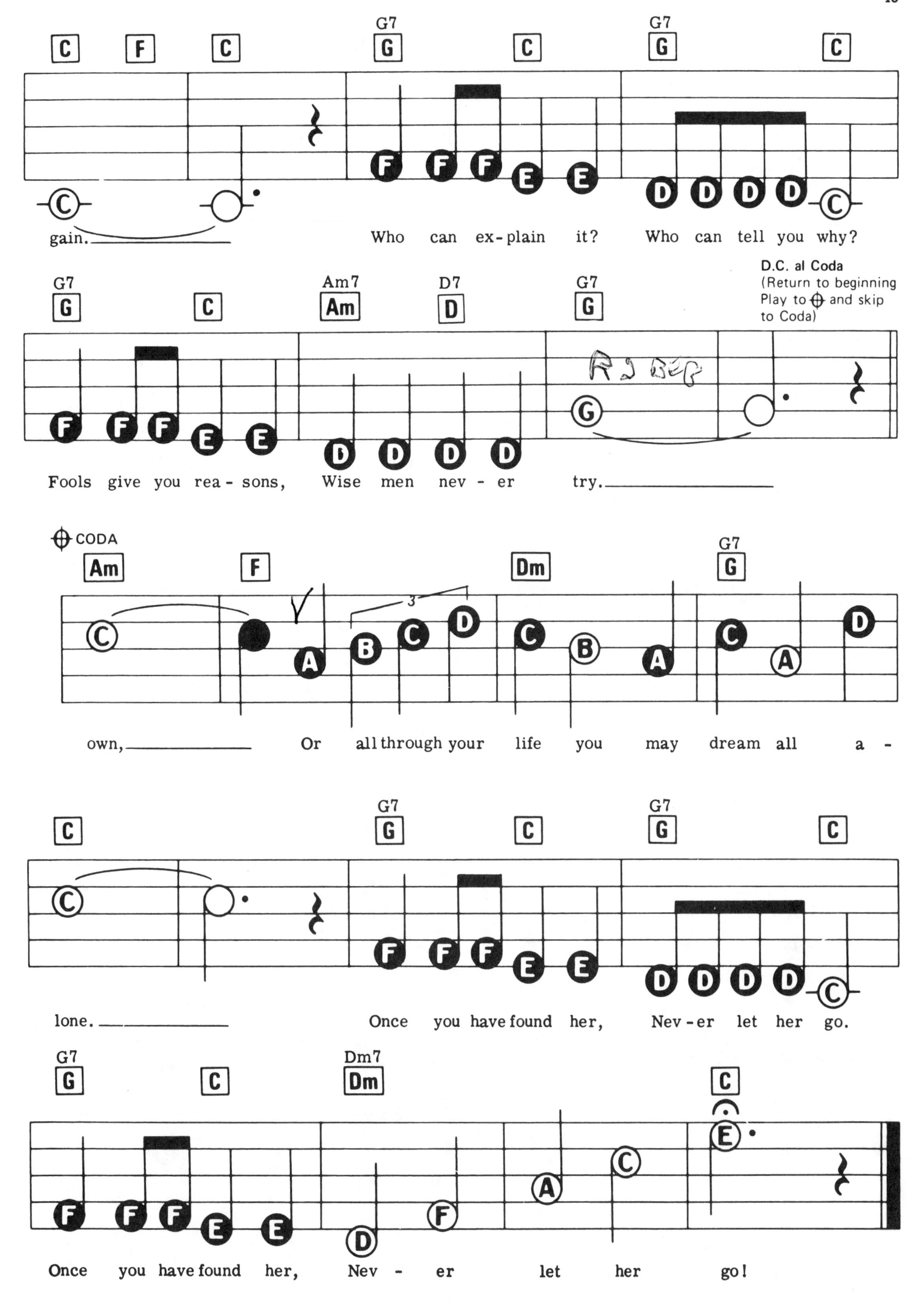
C F C G7 G C G7 G C
gain. Who can ex-plain it? Who can tell you why?
G7 G C Am7 Am D7 D G7 G
D.C. al Coda
(Return to beginning
Play to ⊕ and skip
to Coda)
Fools give you rea-sons, Wise men nev-er try.
⊕ CODA
Am F Dm G7 G
own, Or all through your life you may dream all a-
C G7 G C G7 G C
lone. Once you have found her, Nev-er let her go.
G7 G C Dm7 Dm C
Once you have found her, Nev-er let her go!

Something

Registration 4
Rhythm: Rock

Words and Music by
George Harrison

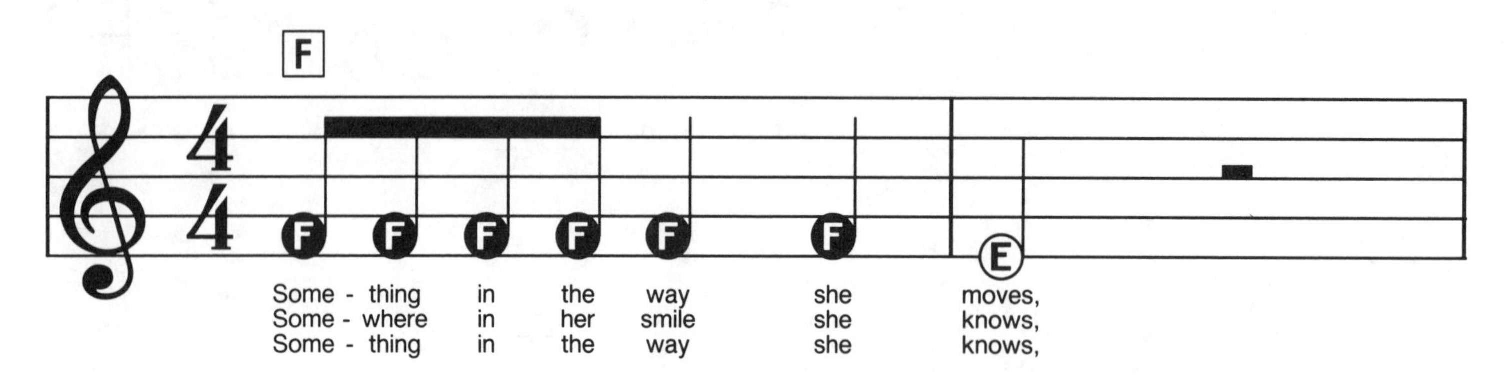

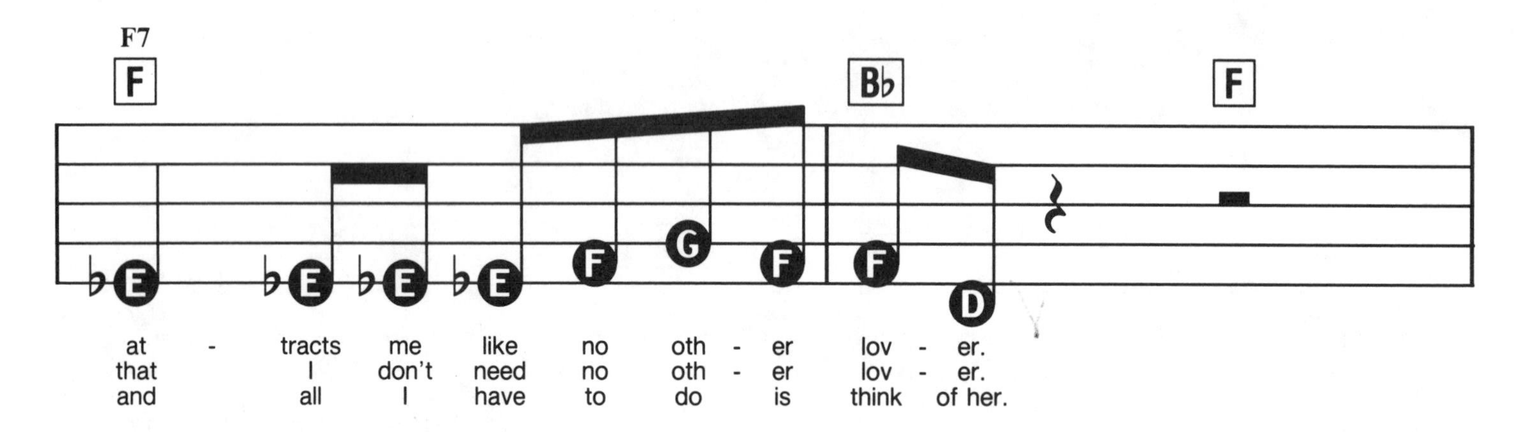

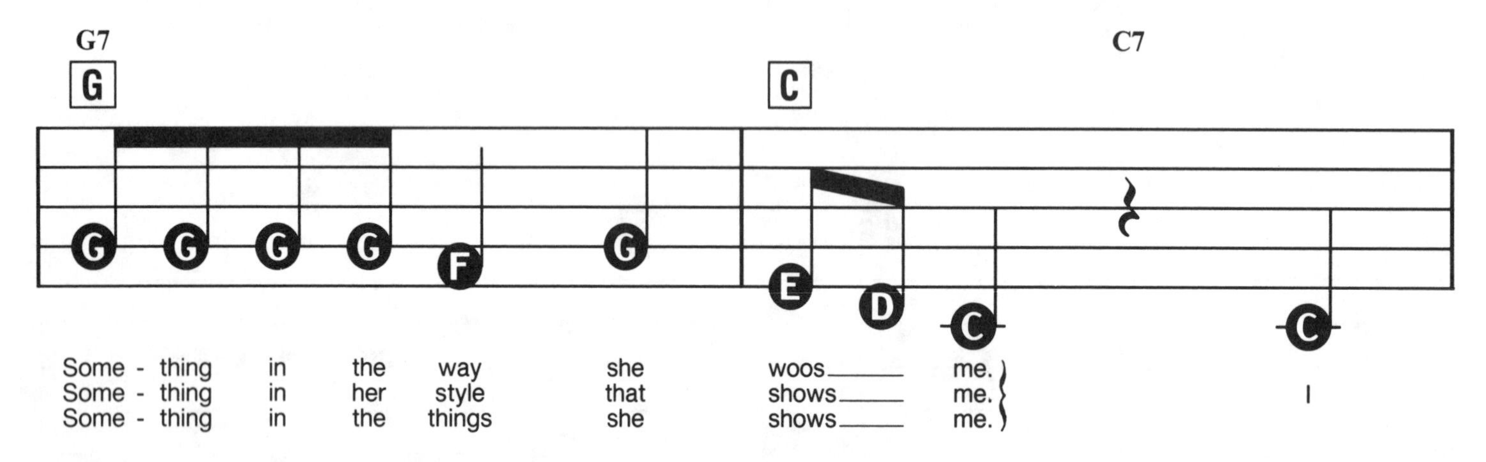

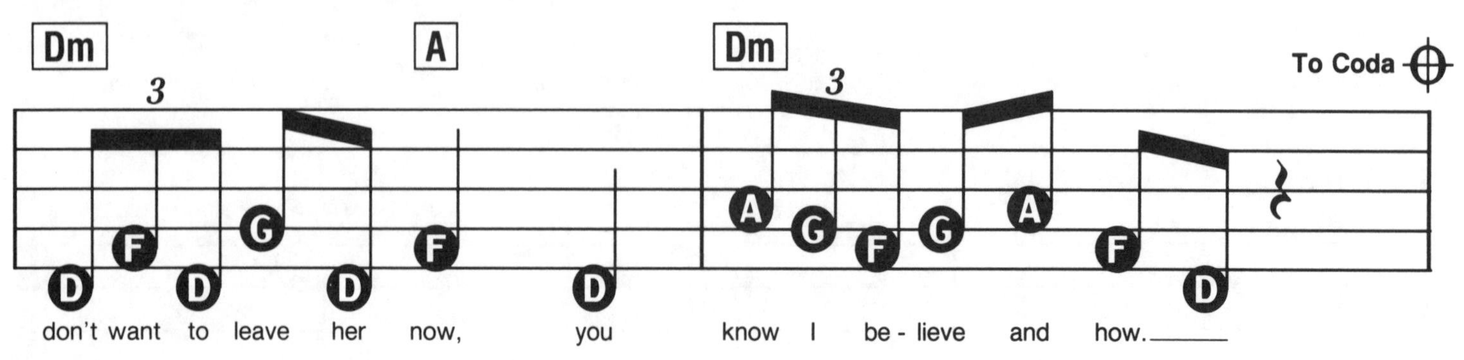

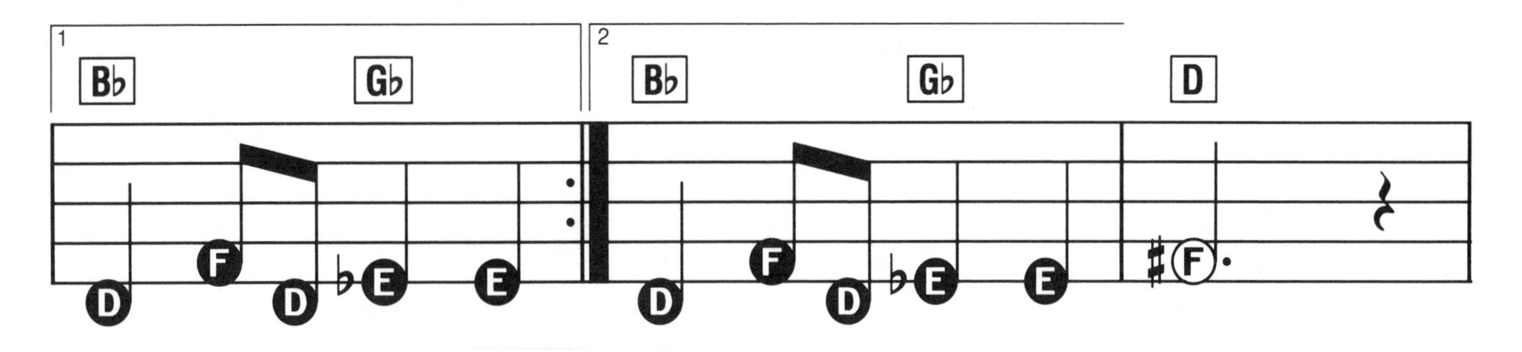
1
B♭ G♭
D F D ♭E E
2
B♭ G♭ D
D F D ♭E E ♯F

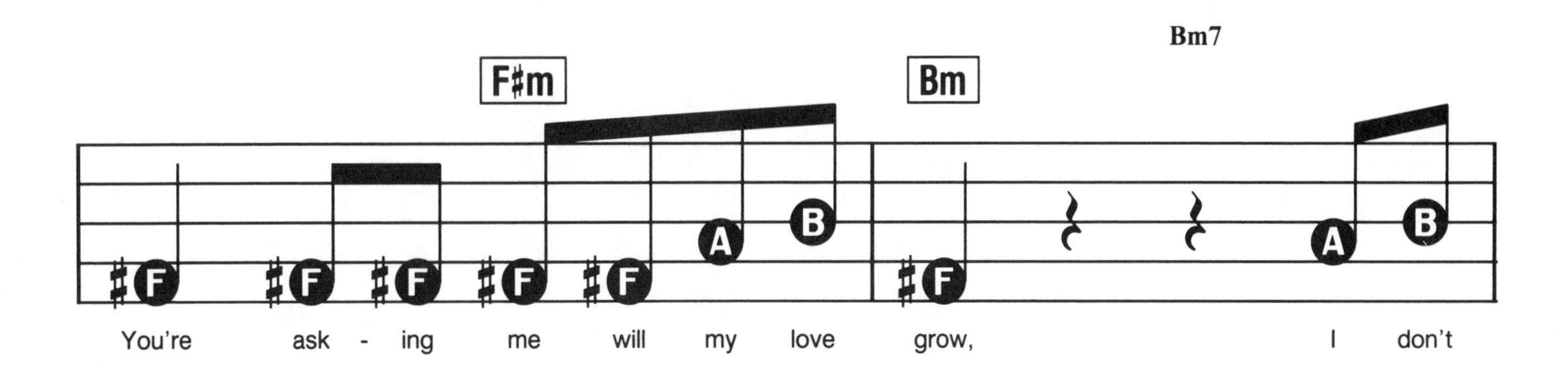
F♯m Bm Bm7
♯F ♯F ♯F ♯F ♯F A B ♯F A B
You're ask - ing me will my love grow, I don't

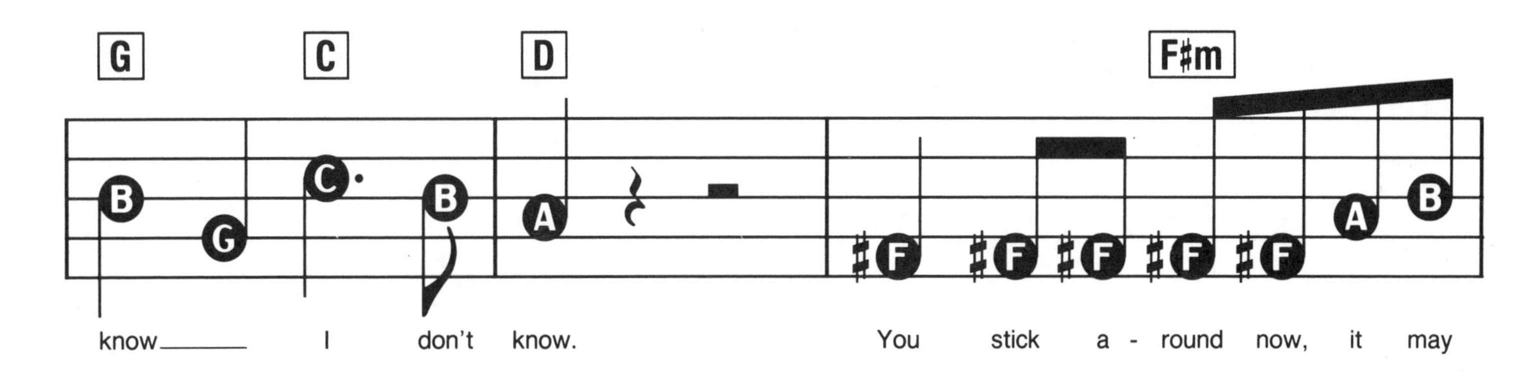
G C D F♯m
B G C B A ♯F ♯F ♯F ♯F ♯F A B
know I don't know. You stick a - round now, it may

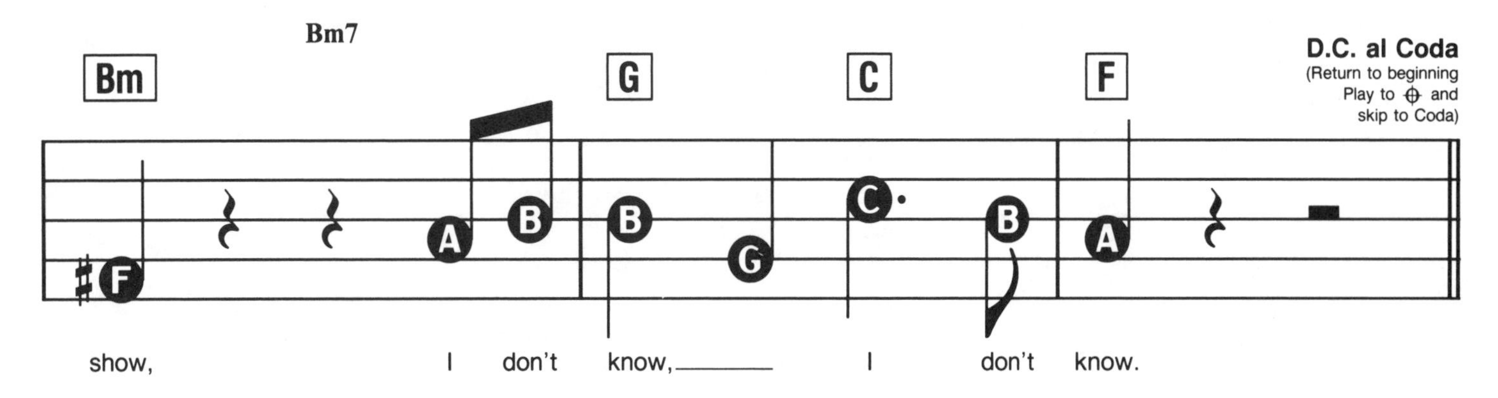
Bm Bm7 G C F
♯F A B B G C B A
show, I don't know, I don't know.
D.C. al Coda
(Return to beginning
Play to ⊕ and
skip to Coda)

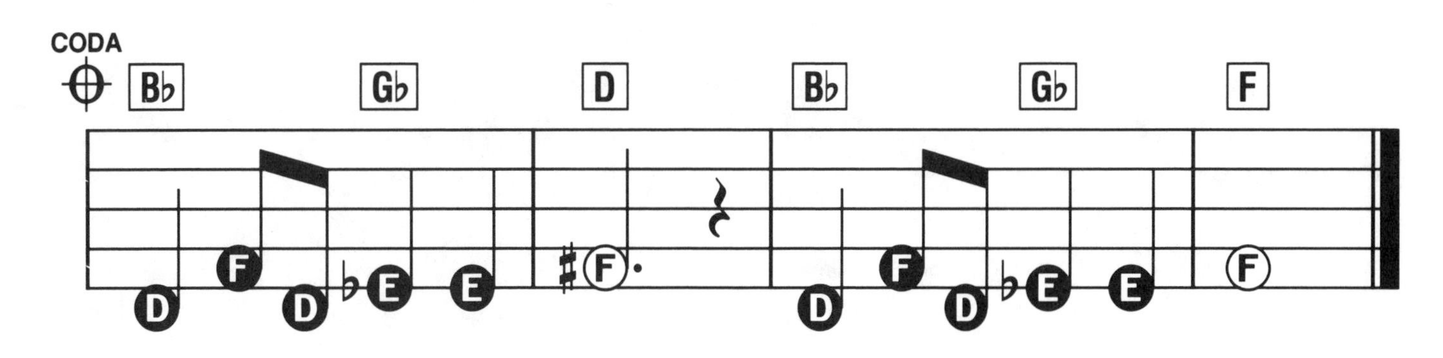
CODA
B♭ G♭ D B♭ G♭ F
D F D ♭E E ♯F D F D ♭E E F

Through the Years

Registration 4
Rhythm: Rock or Slow Rock

Words and Music by
Steve Dorff and Marty Panzer

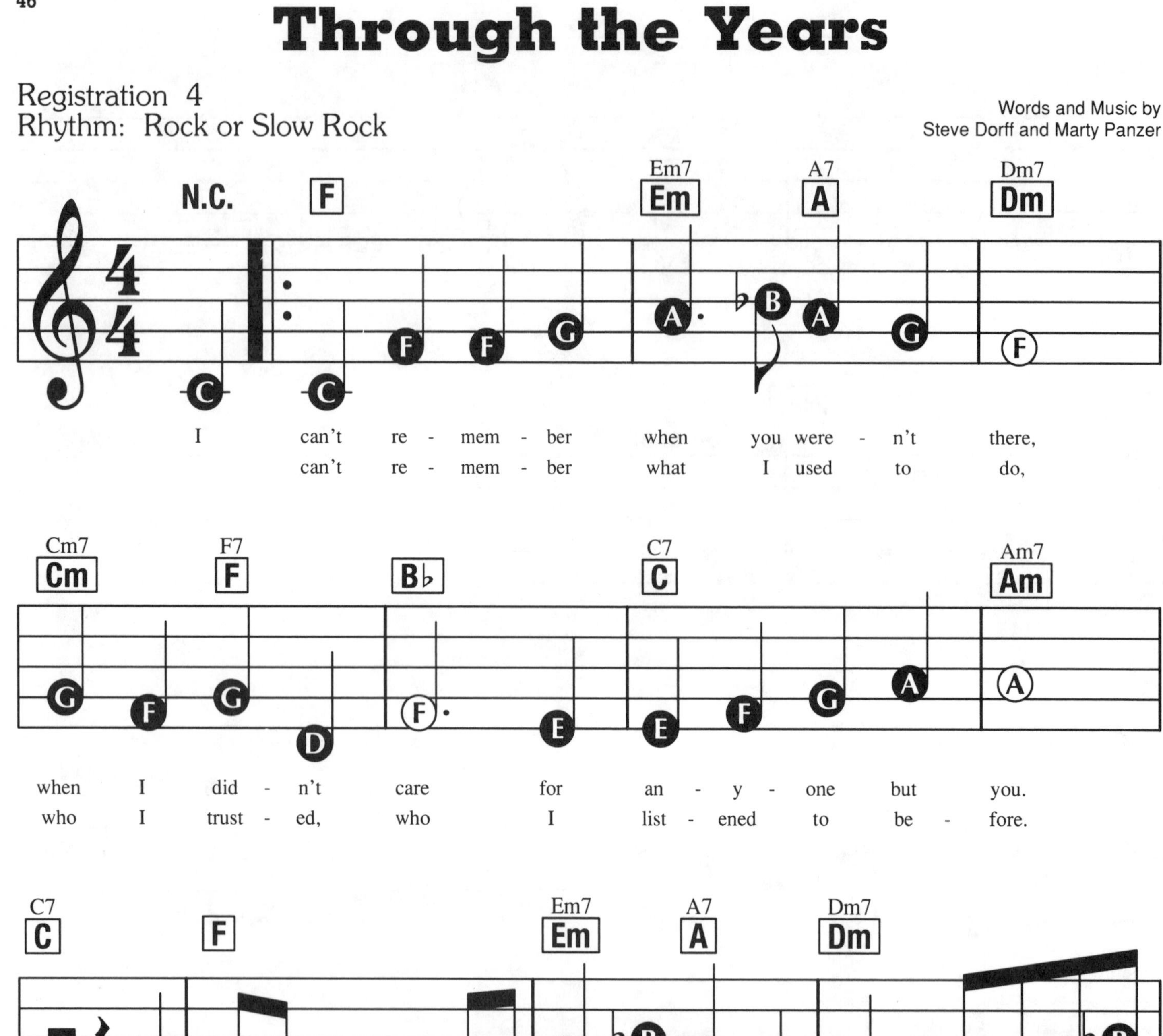

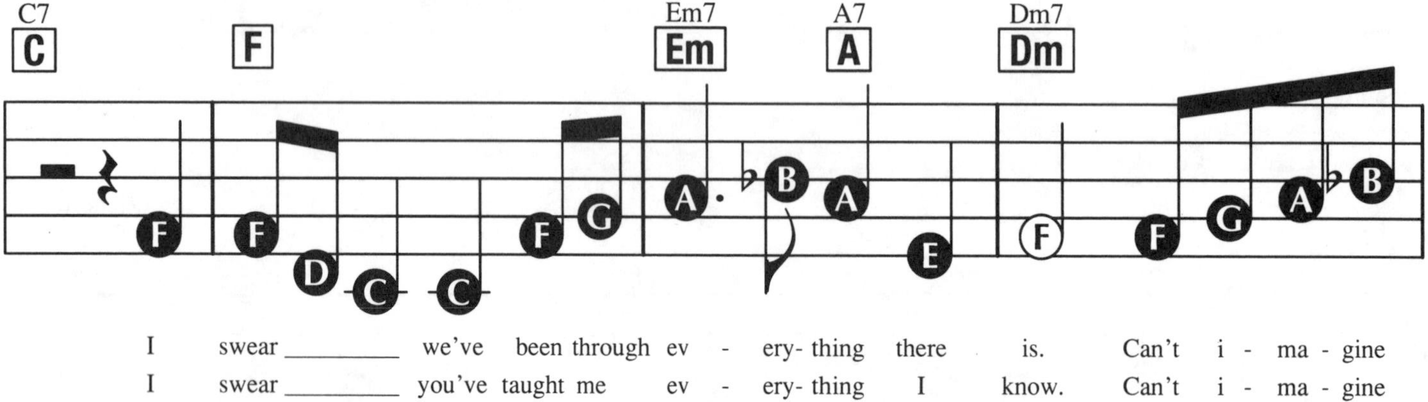

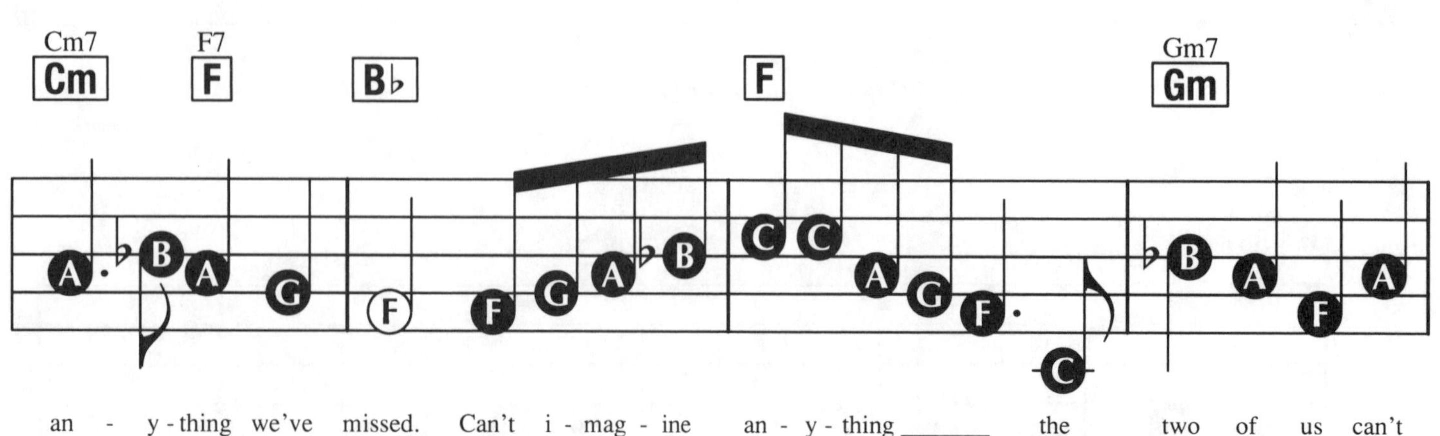

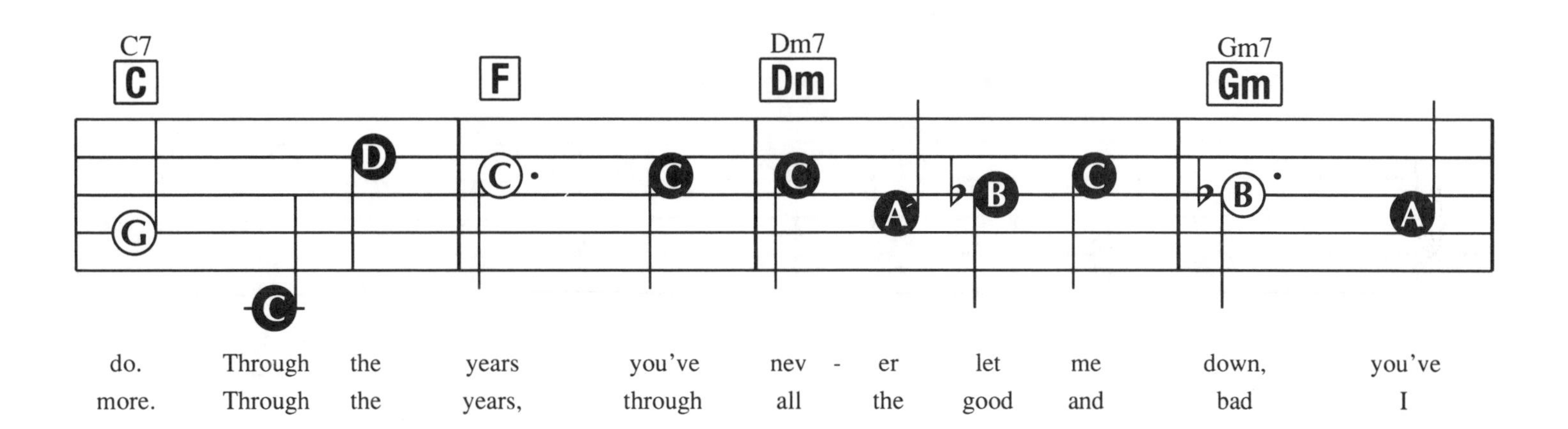
C7 C F Dm7 Dm Gm7 Gm
do. Through the years you've nev - er let me down, you've
more. Through the years, through all the good and bad I

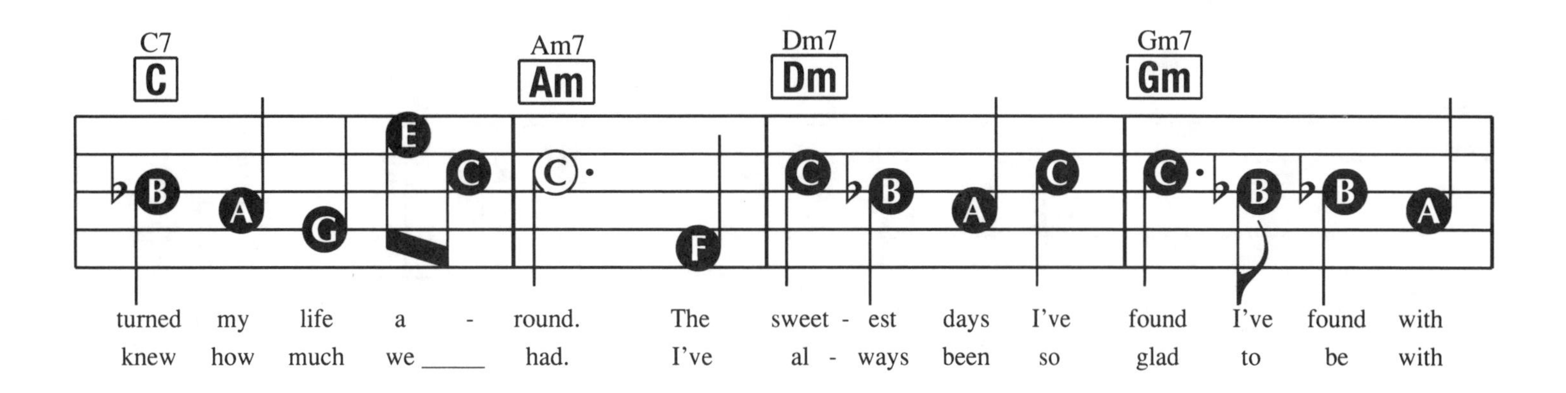
C7 C Am7 Am Dm7 Dm Gm7 Gm
turned my life a - round. The sweet - est days I've found I've found with
knew how much we ___ had. I've al - ways been so glad to be with

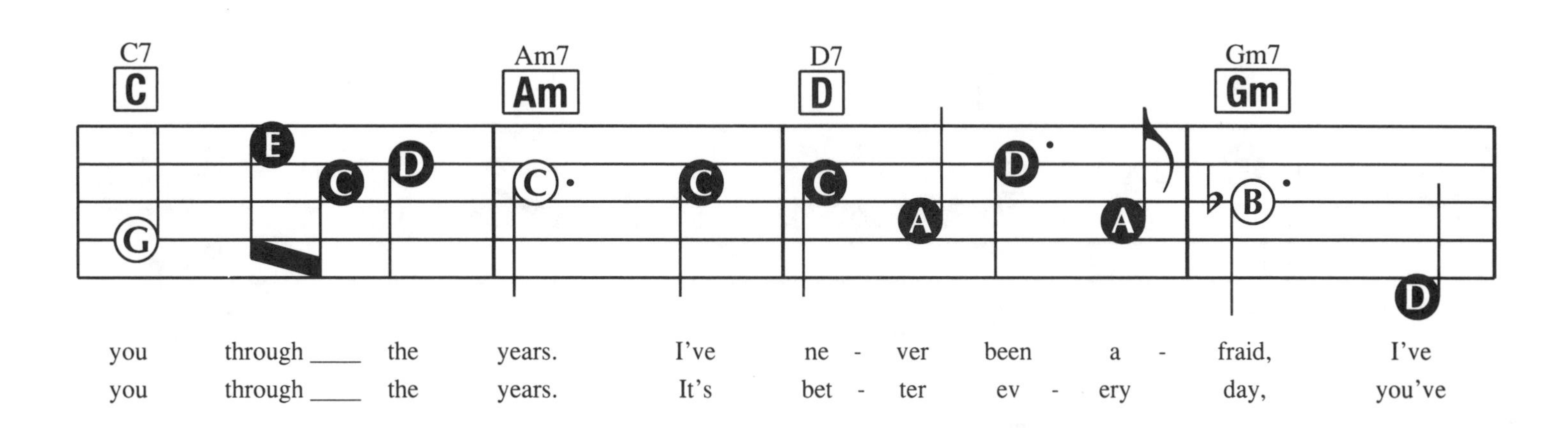
C7 C Am7 Am D7 D Gm7 Gm
you through ___ the years. I've ne - ver been a - fraid, I've
you through ___ the years. It's bet - ter ev - ery day, you've

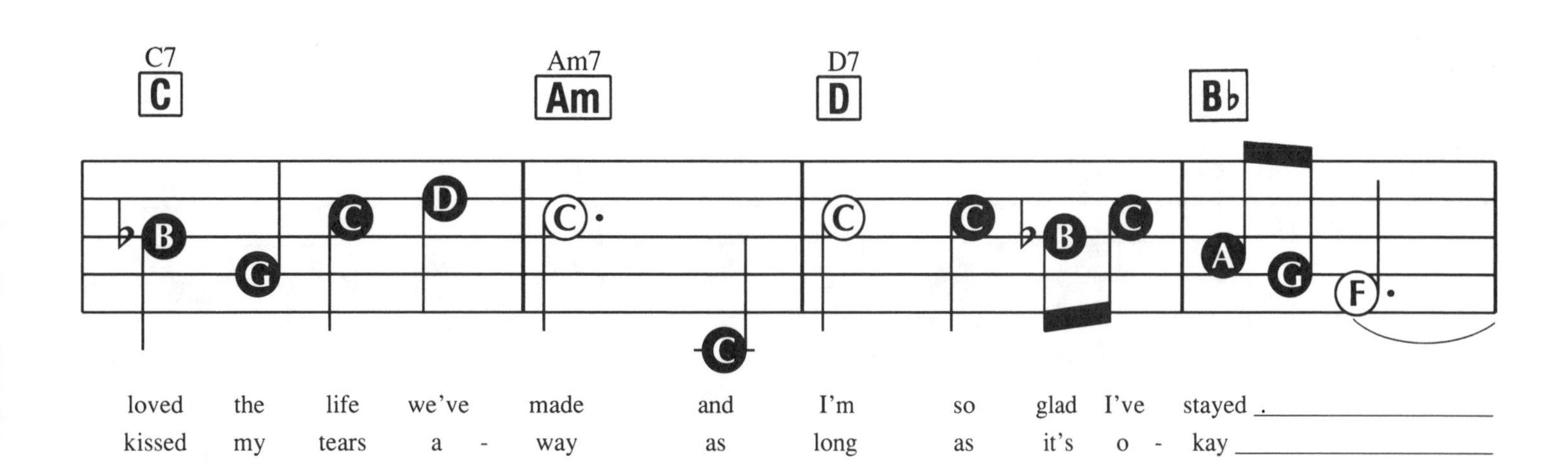
C7 C Am7 Am D7 D B♭
loved the life we've made and I'm so glad I've stayed.
kissed my tears a - way as long as it's o - kay

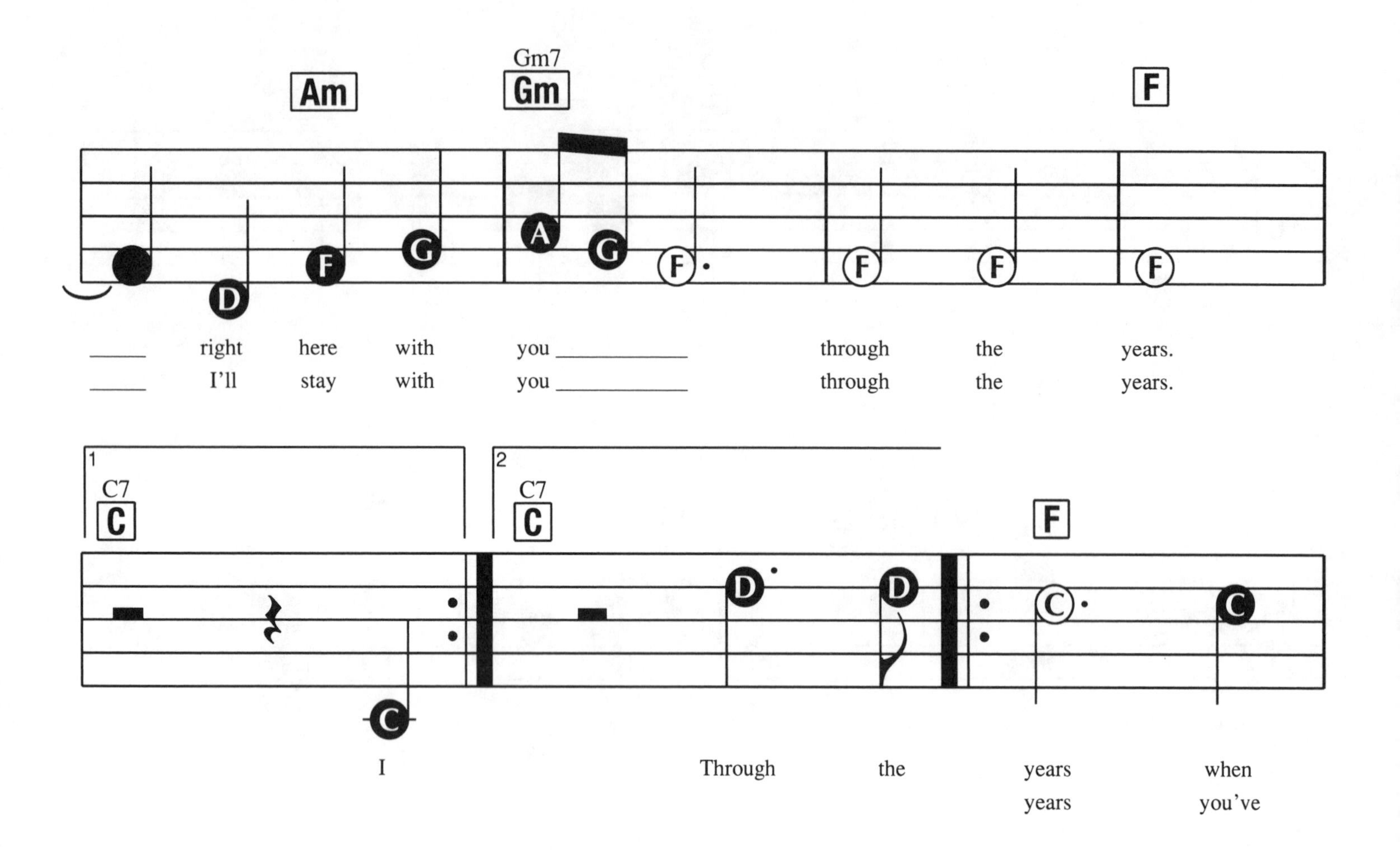
Am
Gm7
Gm
F
D F G A G F F F F
right here with you through the years.
I'll stay with you through the years.
1
C7
C
C
I
2
C7
C
D D
F
C C
Through the years when
years you've

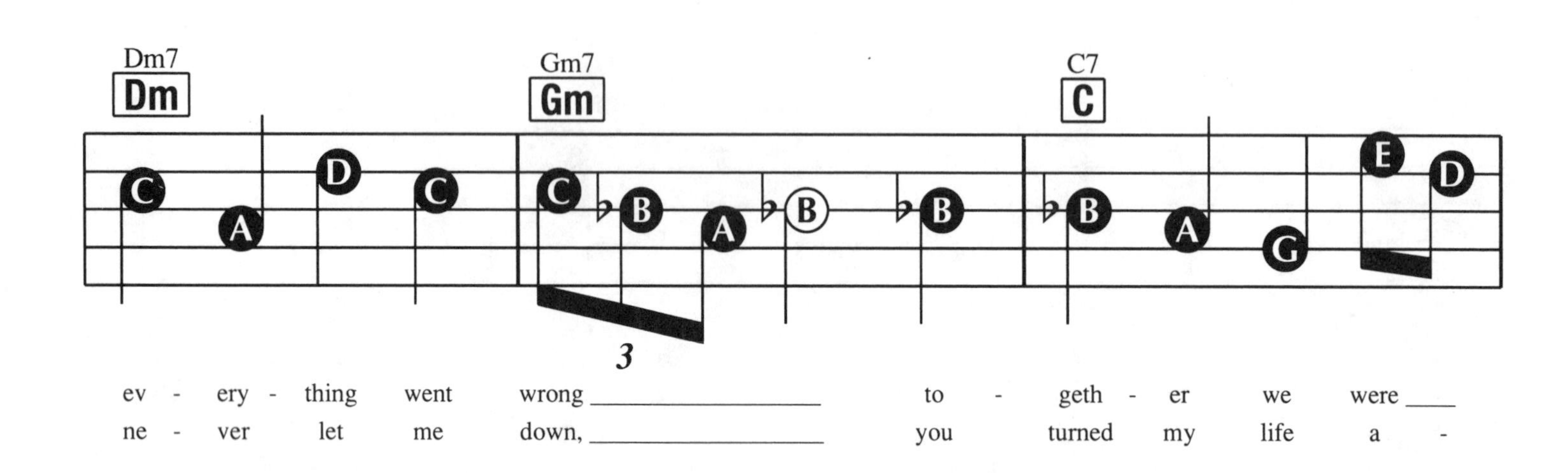
Dm7
Dm
Gm7
Gm
C7
C
C A D C C B A B B B A G E D
3
ev - ery - thing went wrong to - geth - er we were
ne - ver let me down, you turned my life a -

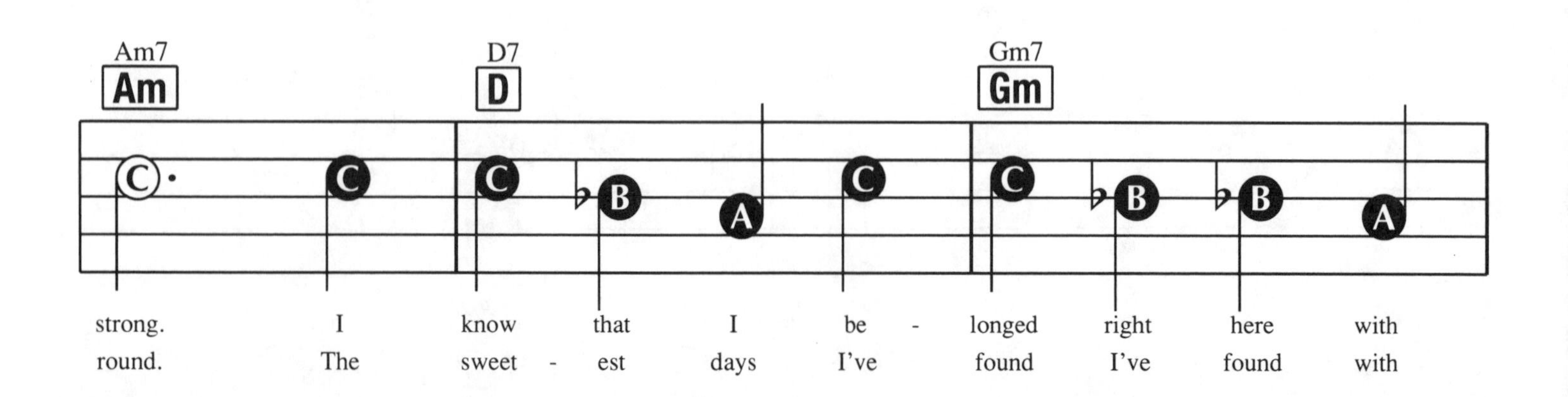
Am7
Am
D7
D
Gm7
Gm
C C C B A C C B B A
strong. I know that I be - longed right here with
round. The sweet - est days I've found I've found with

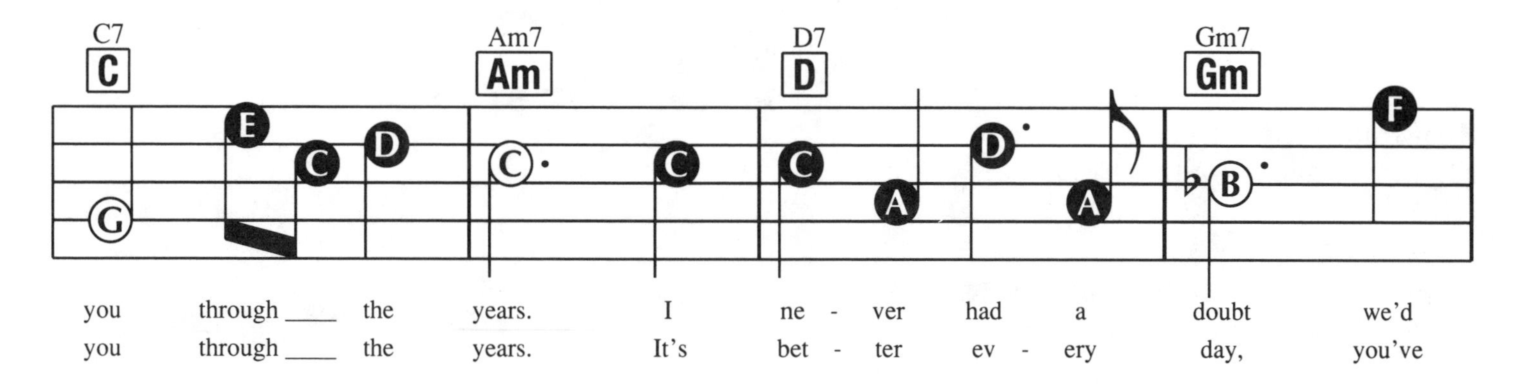
C7
C
Am7
Am
D7
D
Gm7
Gm
G
E
C
D
C
C
C
A
D
A
B
F
you through ___ the years. I ne - ver had a doubt we'd
you through ___ the years. It's bet - ter ev - ery day, you've

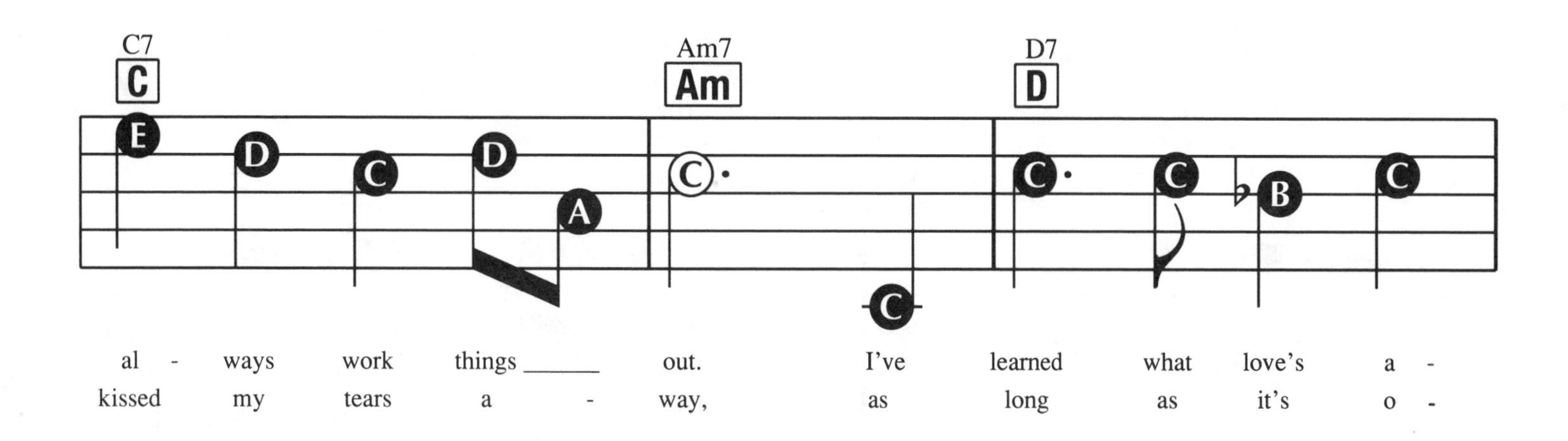
C7
C
Am7
Am
D7
D
E
D
C
D
A
C
C
C
C
B
C
al - ways work things ______ out. I've learned what love's a -
kissed my tears a - way, as long as it's o -

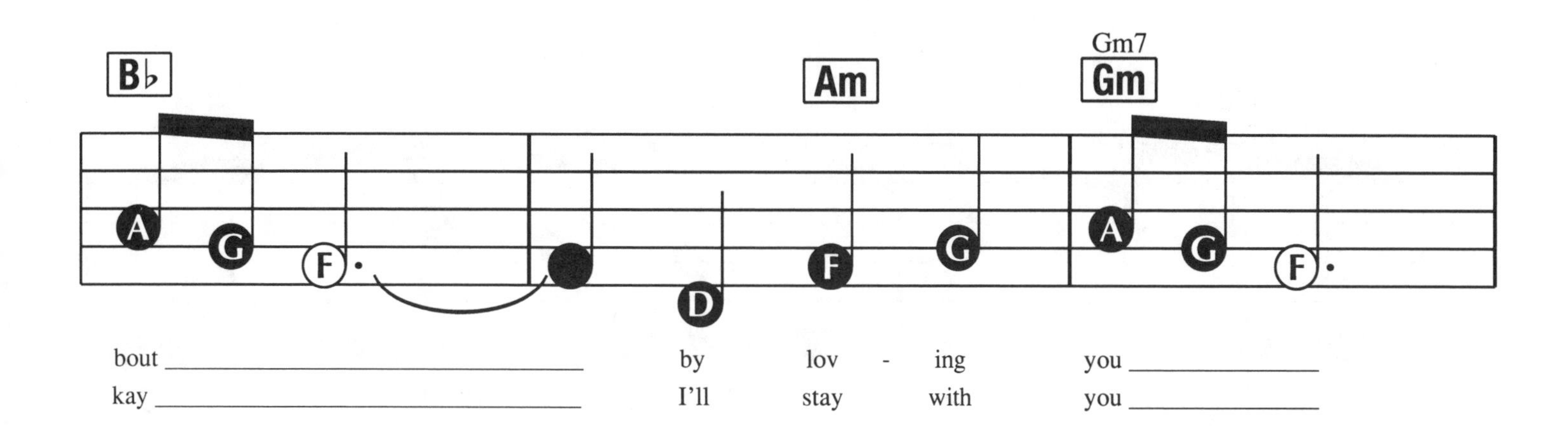
B♭
Am
Gm7
Gm
A
G
F
D
F
G
A
G
F
bout ________ by lov - ing you ______
kay ________ I'll stay with you ______

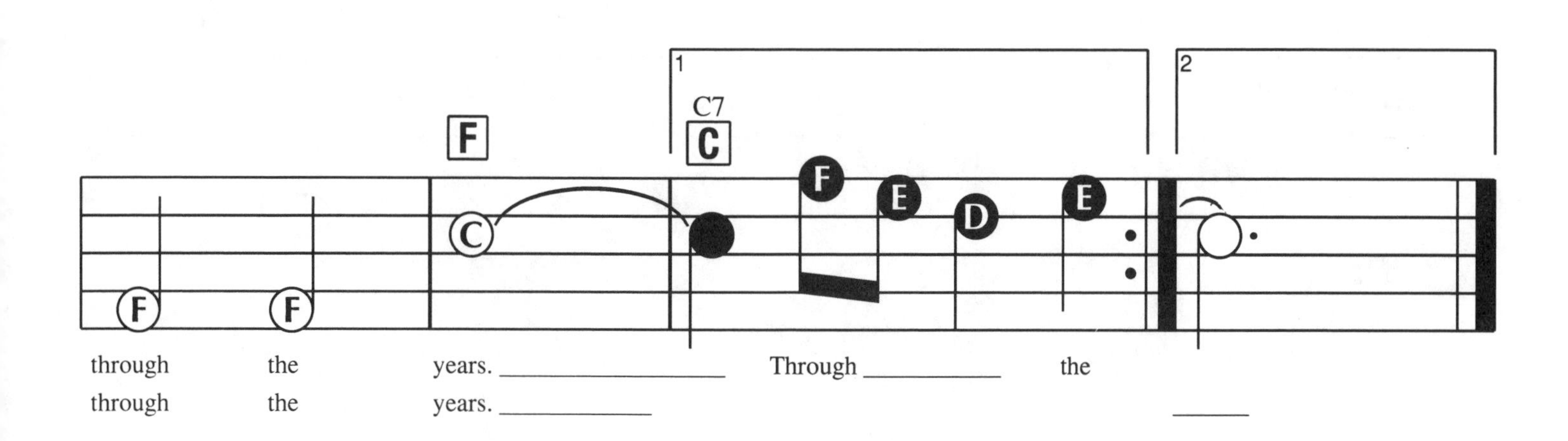
F
1
C7
C
2
F
F
C
F
E
D
E
through the years. ______ Through ______ the
through the years. ______ ______

Where Do I Begin

(Love Theme)

from the Paramount Picture LOVE STORY

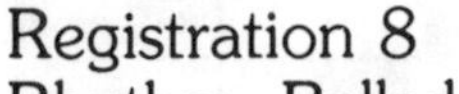

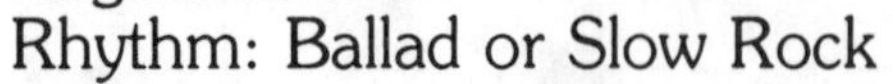

Words by Carl Sigman
Music by Francis Lai

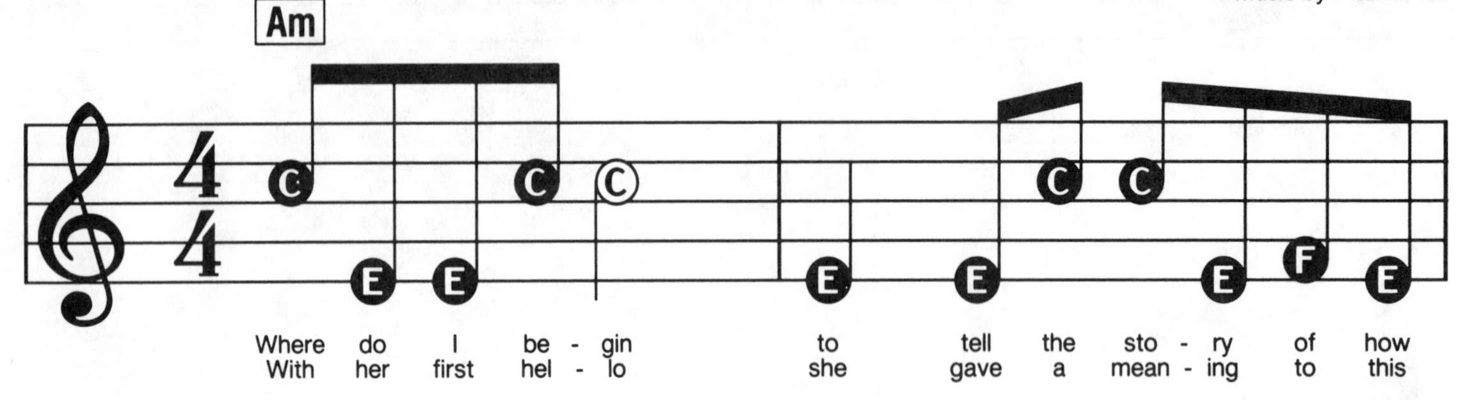

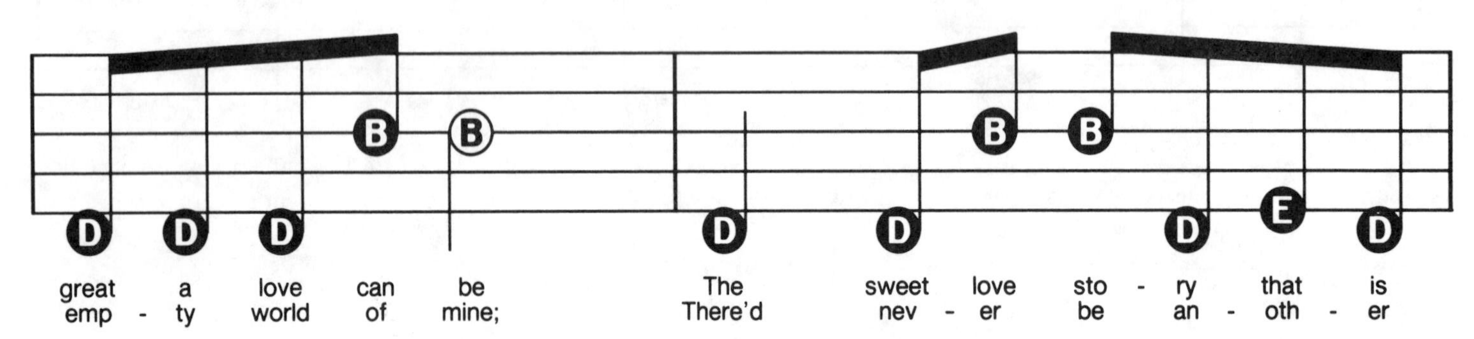

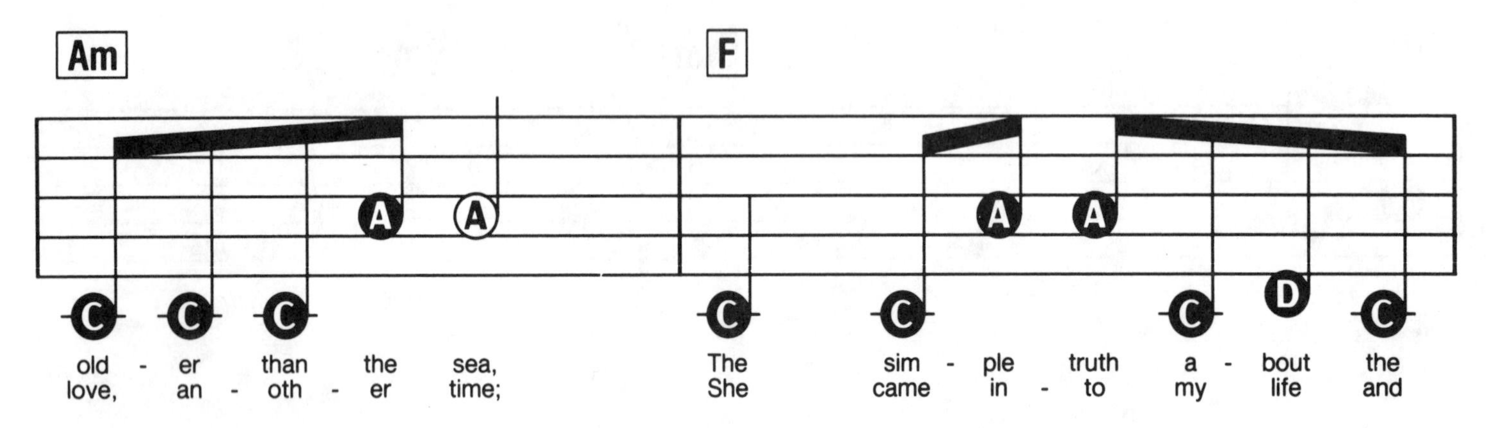

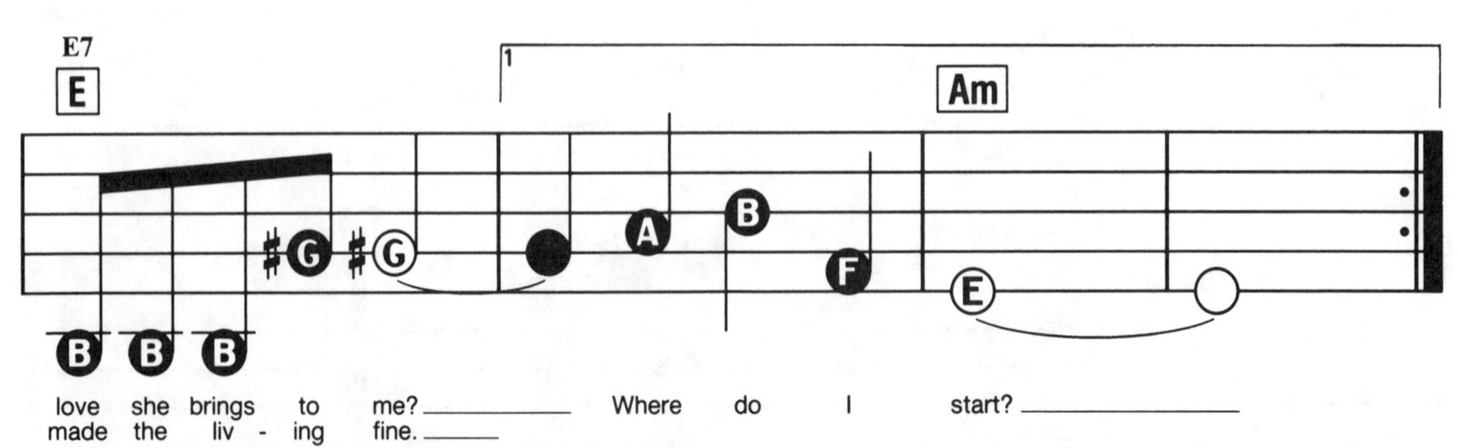

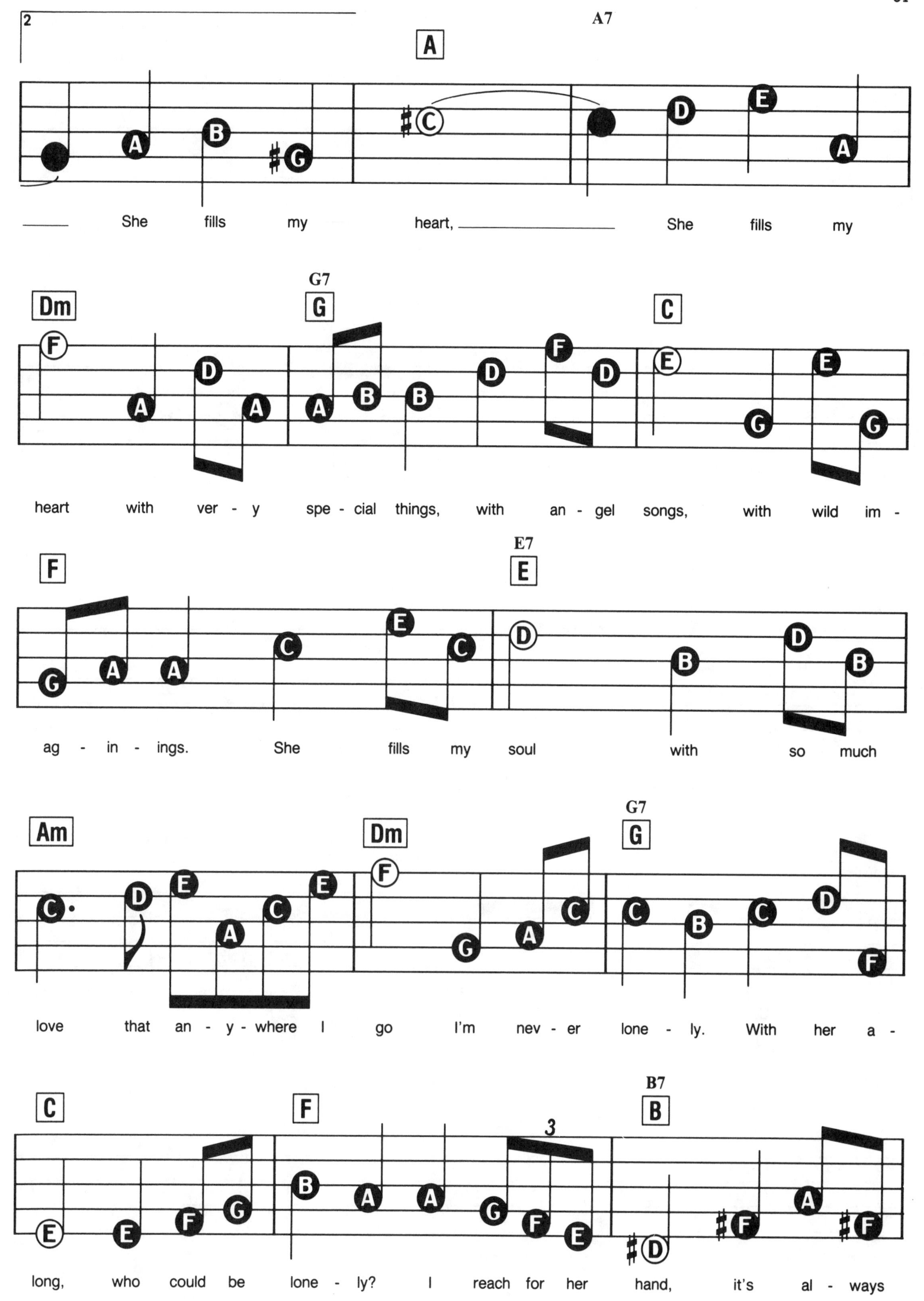
2
A7
A
She fills my heart, She fills my
Dm
G7
G
C
heart with ver - y spe - cial things, with an - gel songs, with wild im -
F
E7
E
ag - in - ings. She fills my soul with so much
Am
Dm
G7
G
love that an - y - where I go I'm nev - er lone - ly. With her a -
C
F
B7
B
3
long, who could be lone - ly? I reach for her hand, it's al - ways

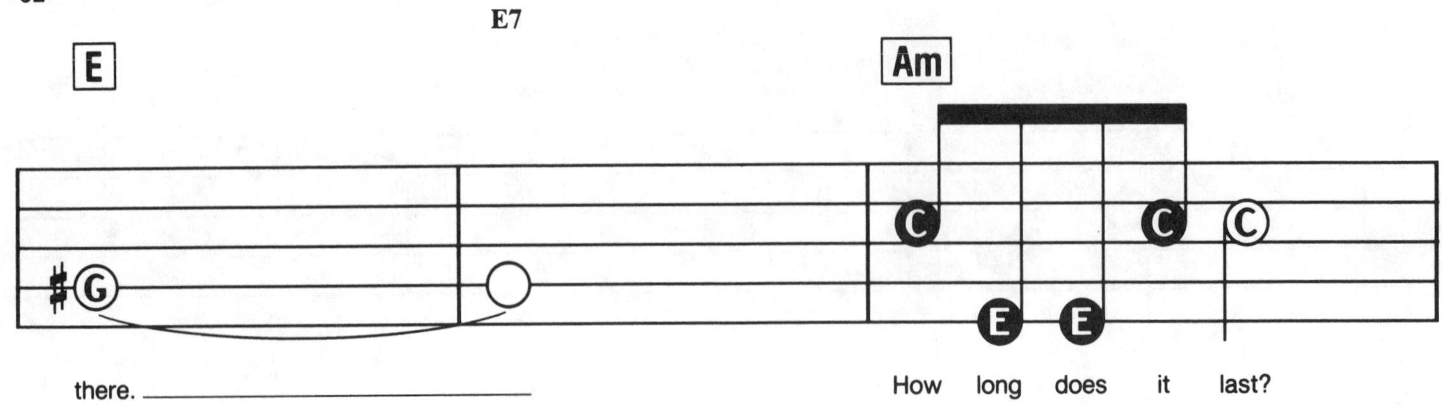
E
E7
Am
there. ___ How long does it last?

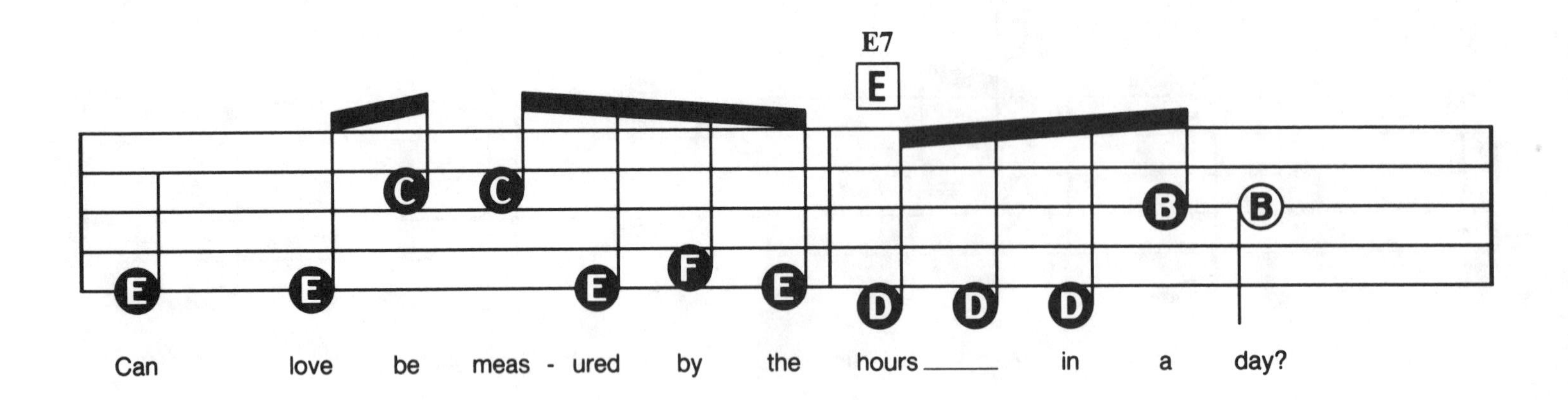
E7
E
Can love be meas - ured by the hours ___ in a day?

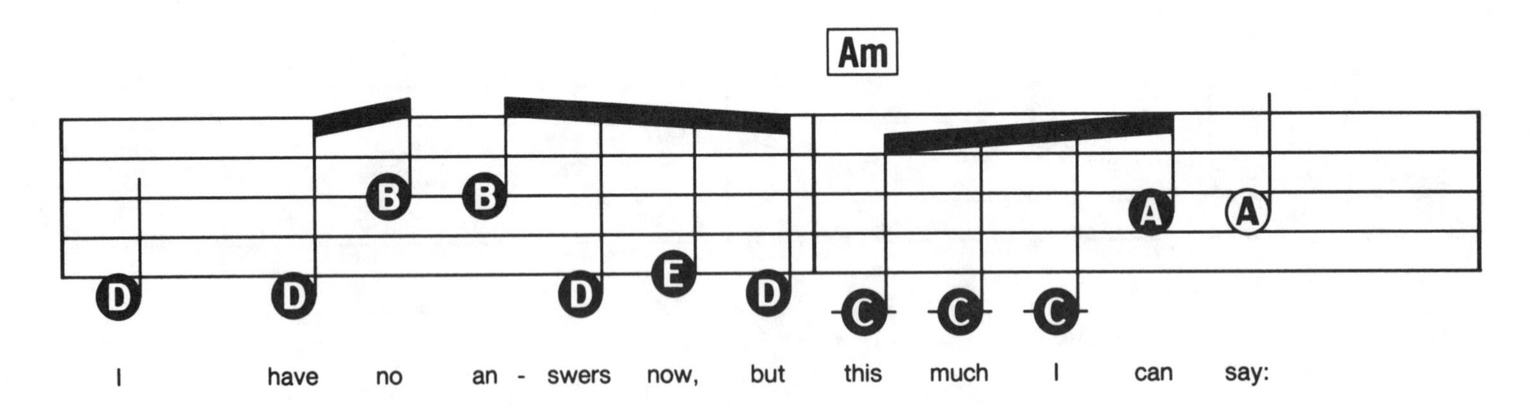
Am
I have no an - swers now, but this much I can say:

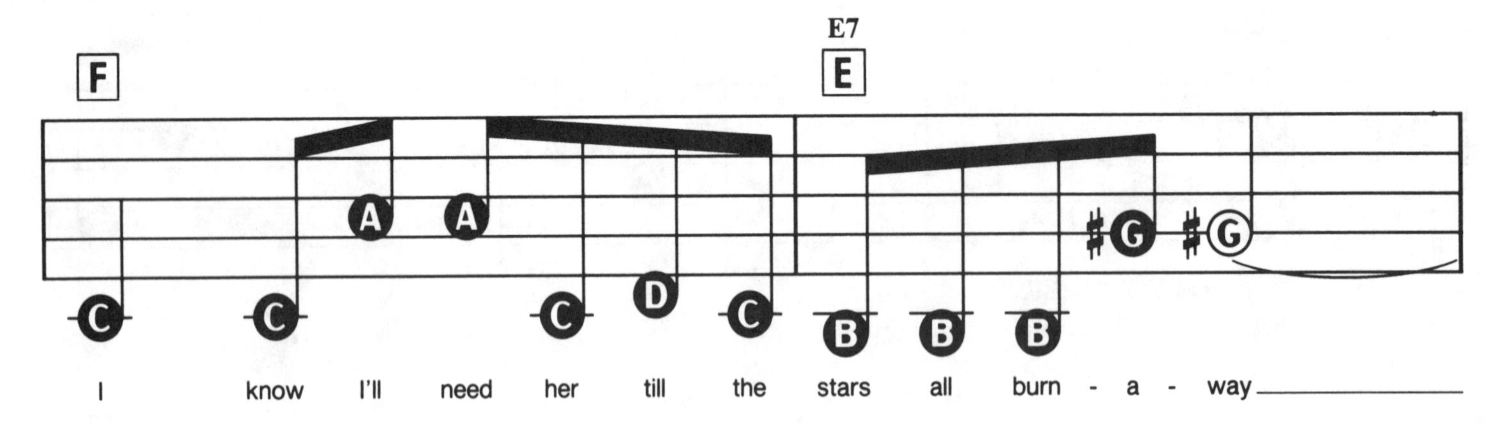
F
E7
E
I know I'll need her till the stars all burn - a - way ___

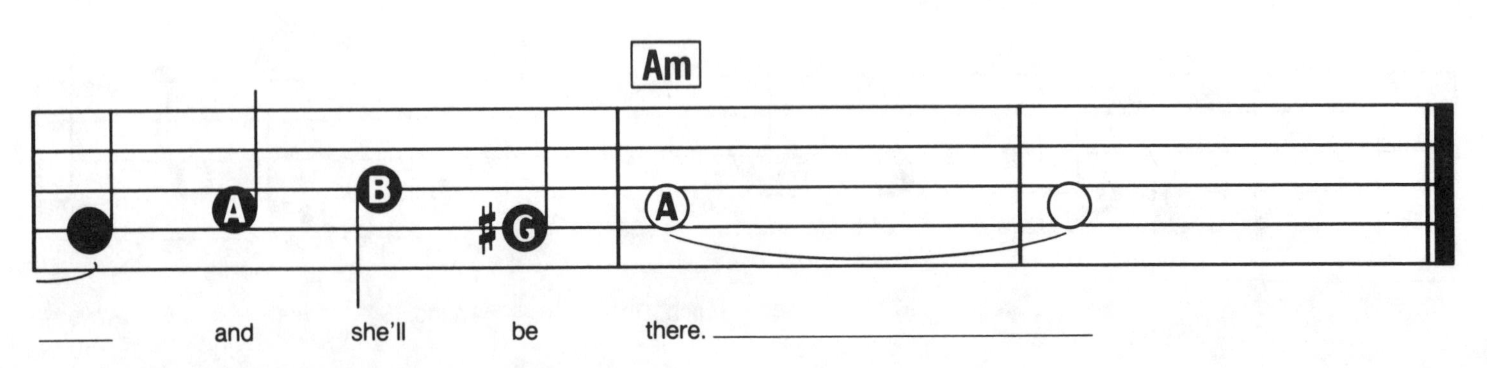
Am
___ and she'll be there. ___

Woman

Registration 3
Rhythm: Rock or Jazz Rock

Words and Music by
John Lennon

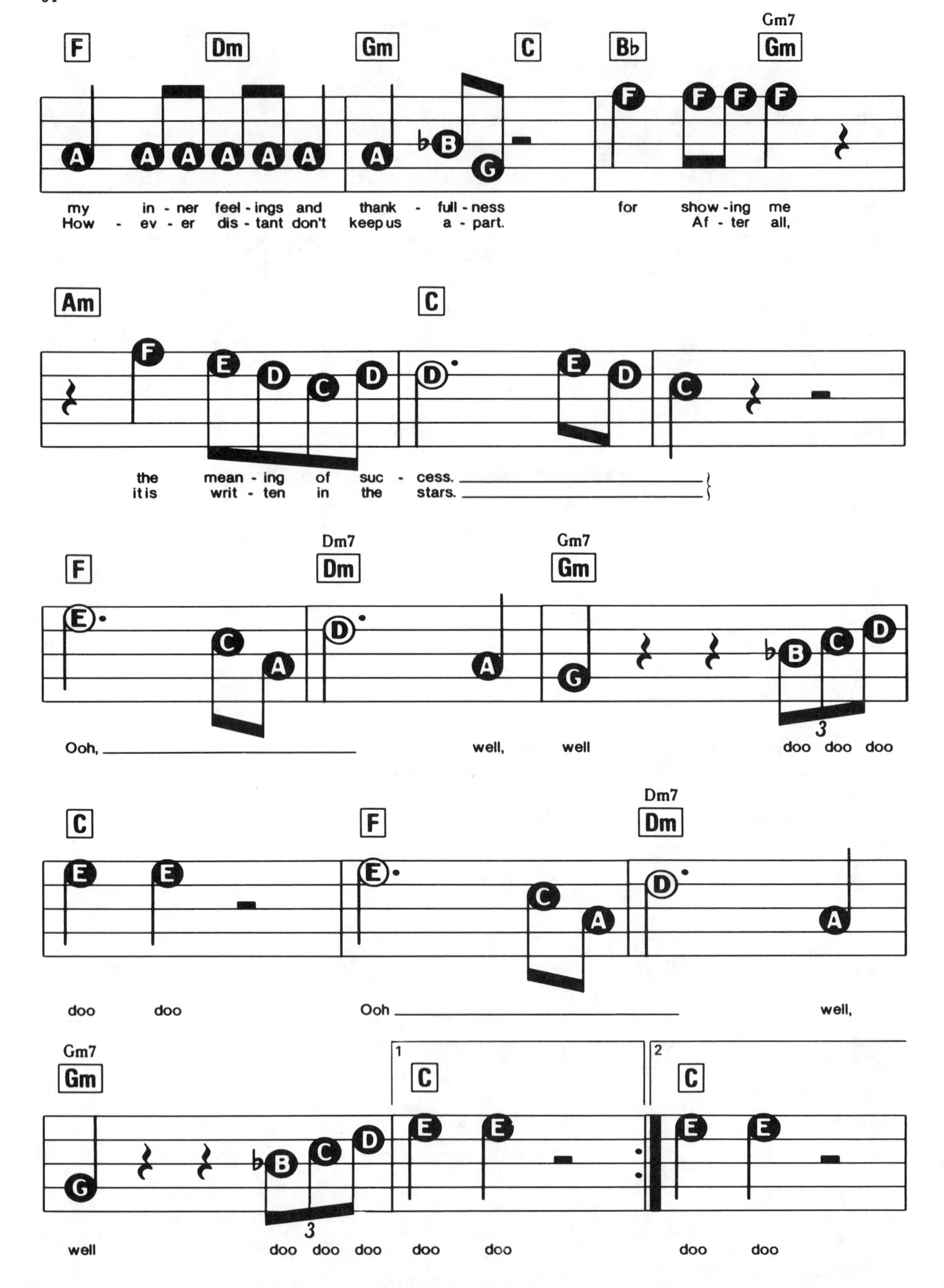
F
Dm
Gm
C
Bb
Gm7
Gm
my in - ner feel - ings and thank - full - ness for show - ing me
How - ev - er dis - tant don't keep us a - part. Af - ter all,
Am
C
the mean - ing of suc - cess.
it is writ - ten in the stars.
F
Dm7
Dm
Gm7
Gm
Ooh, well, well doo doo doo
3
C
F
Dm7
Dm
doo doo Ooh well,
Gm7
Gm
1
C
2
C
well doo doo doo doo doo doo doo
3

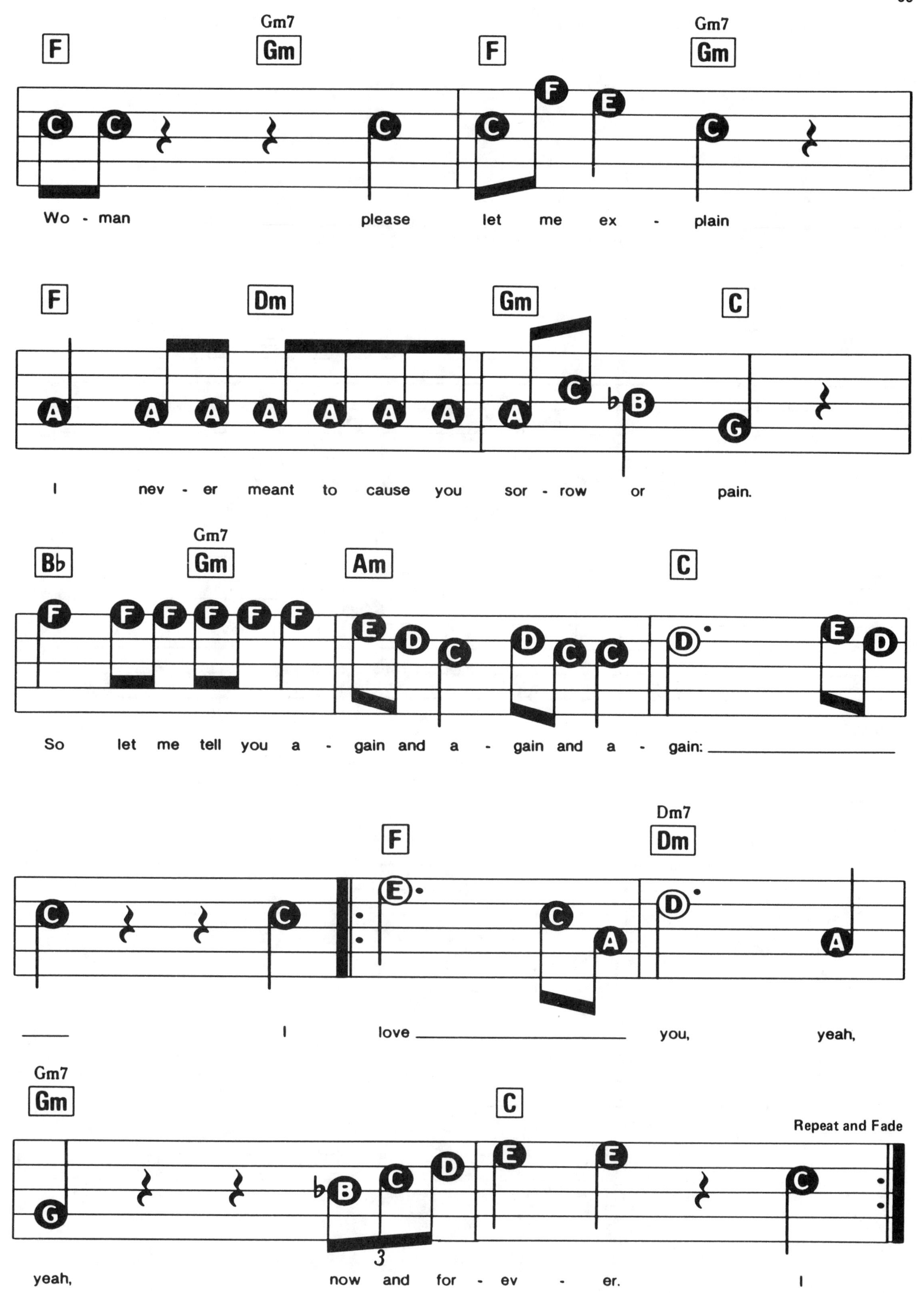
F
Gm7
Gm
F
Gm7
Gm
Wo - man please let me ex - plain
F
Dm
Gm
C
I nev - er meant to cause you sor - row or pain.
B♭
Gm7
Gm
Am
C
So let me tell you a - gain and a - gain and a - gain:
F
Dm7
Dm
I love you, yeah,
Gm7
Gm
C
Repeat and Fade
yeah, now and for - ev - er. I

You Give Good Love

Registration 5
Rhythm: Rock

Words and Music by
La Forrest "La La" Cope

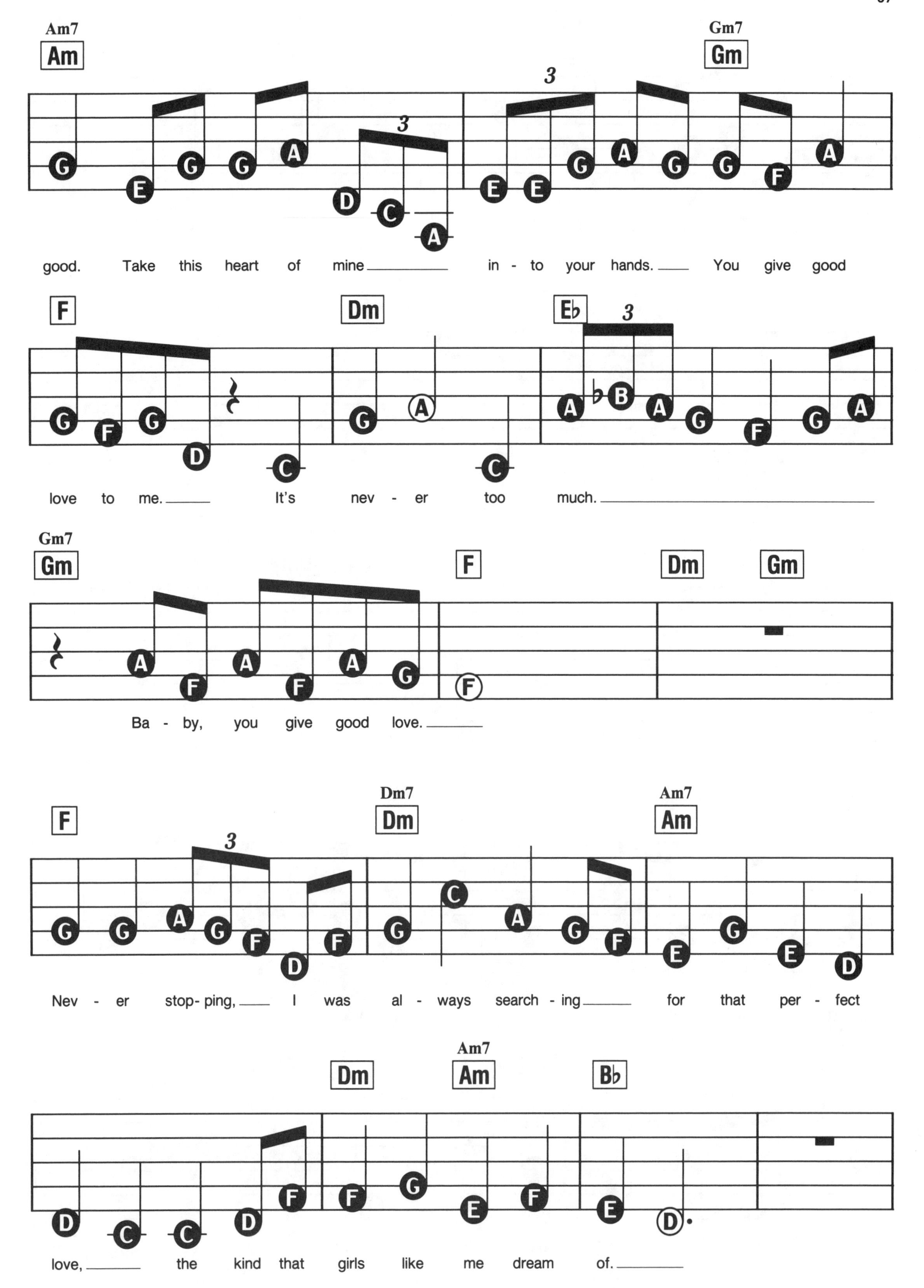
Am7
Am
Gm7
Gm
good. Take this heart of mine in - to your hands. You give good
F
Dm
E♭
love to me. It's nev - er too much.
Gm7
Gm
F
Dm
Gm
Ba - by, you give good love.
F
Dm7
Dm
Am7
Am
Nev - er stop- ping, I was al - ways search - ing for that per - fect
Dm
Am7
Am
B♭
love, the kind that girls like me dream of.

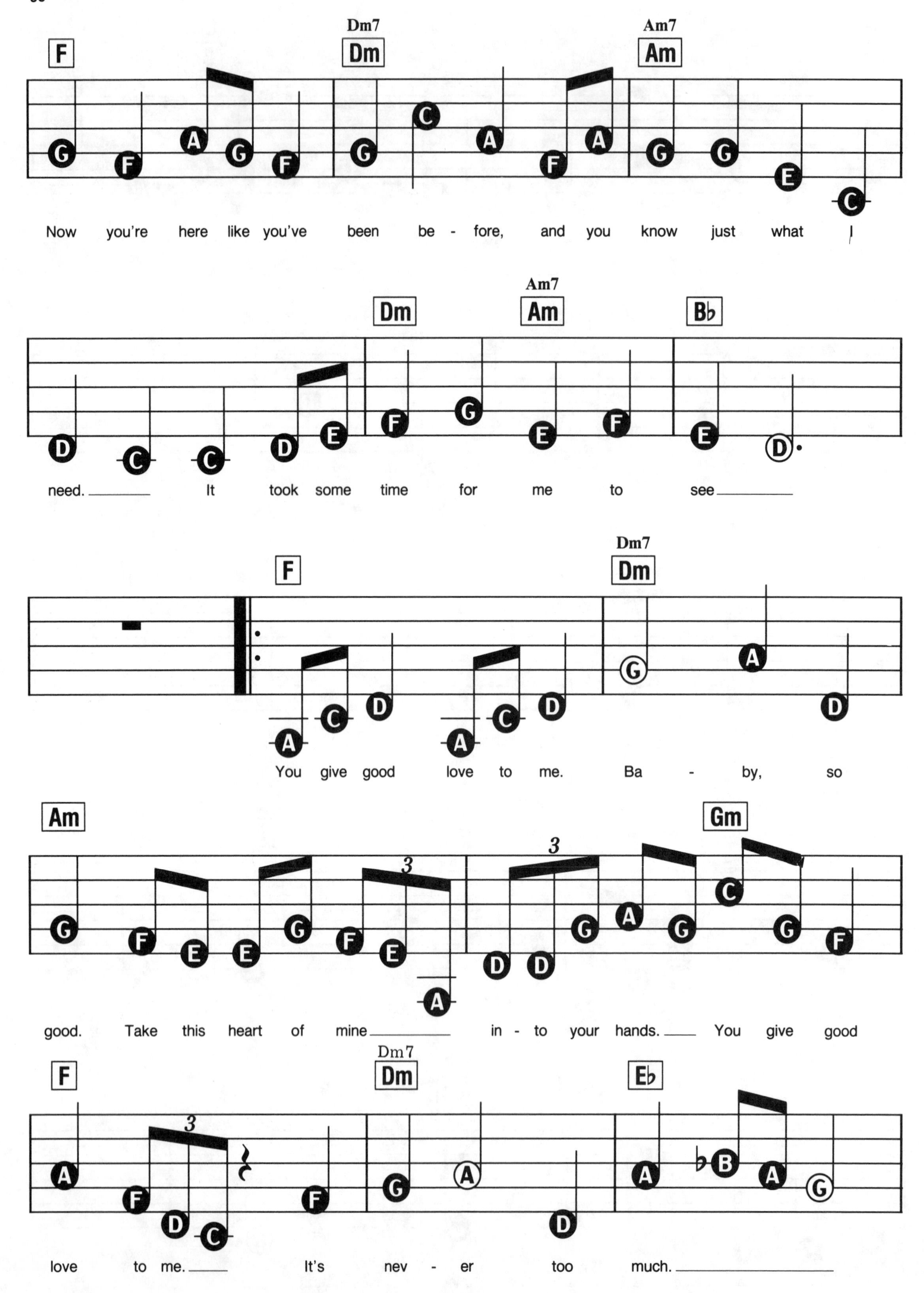
F
Dm7
Dm
Am7
Am
Now you're here like you've been be - fore, and you know just what I
Dm
Am7
Am
B♭
need. It took some time for me to see
F
Dm7
Dm
You give good love to me. Ba - by, so
Am
Gm
good. Take this heart of mine in - to your hands. You give good
F
Dm7
Dm
E♭
love to me. It's nev - er too much.

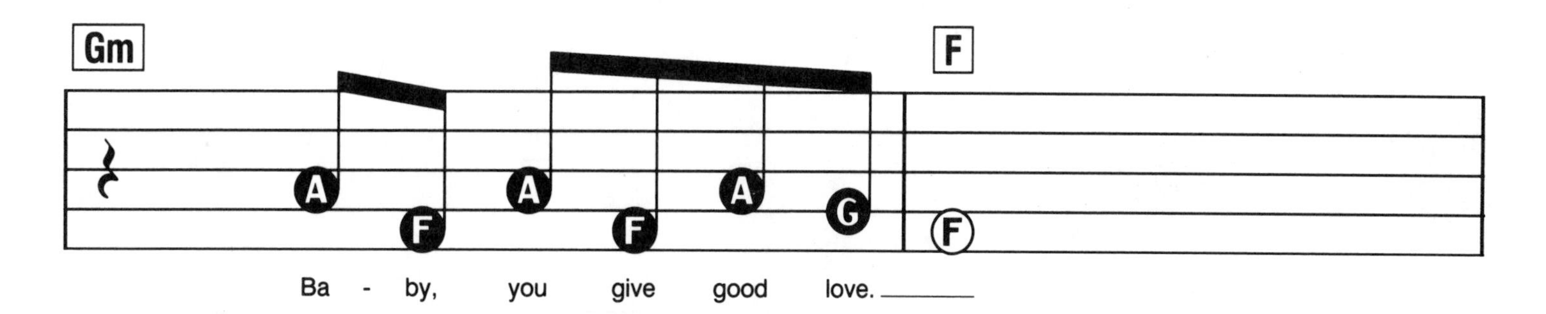
Gm
F
Ba - by, you give good love.

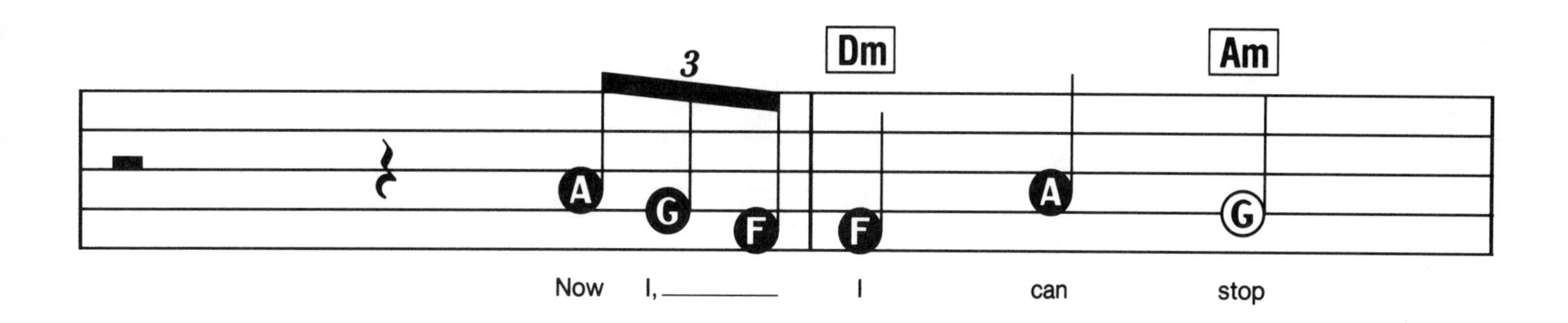
3
Dm
Am
Now I, I can stop

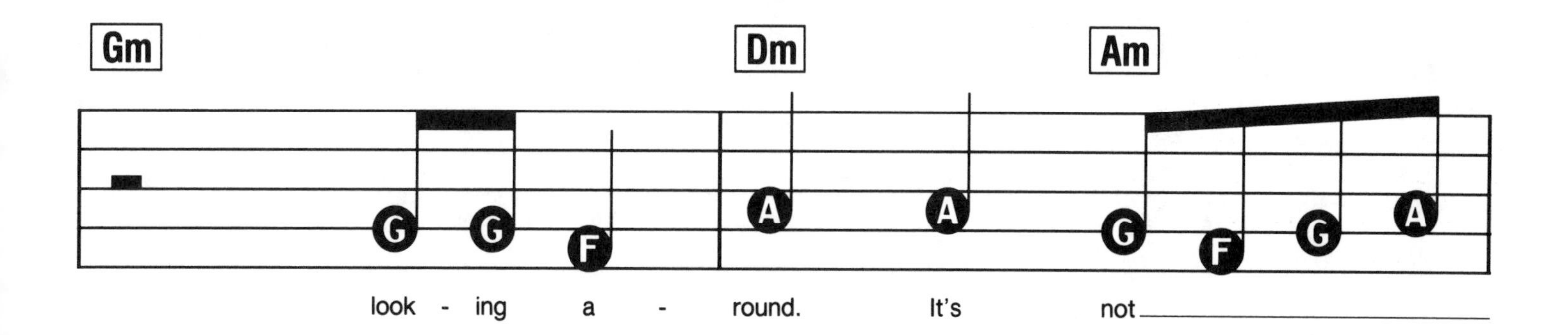
Gm
Dm
Am
look - ing a - round. It's not

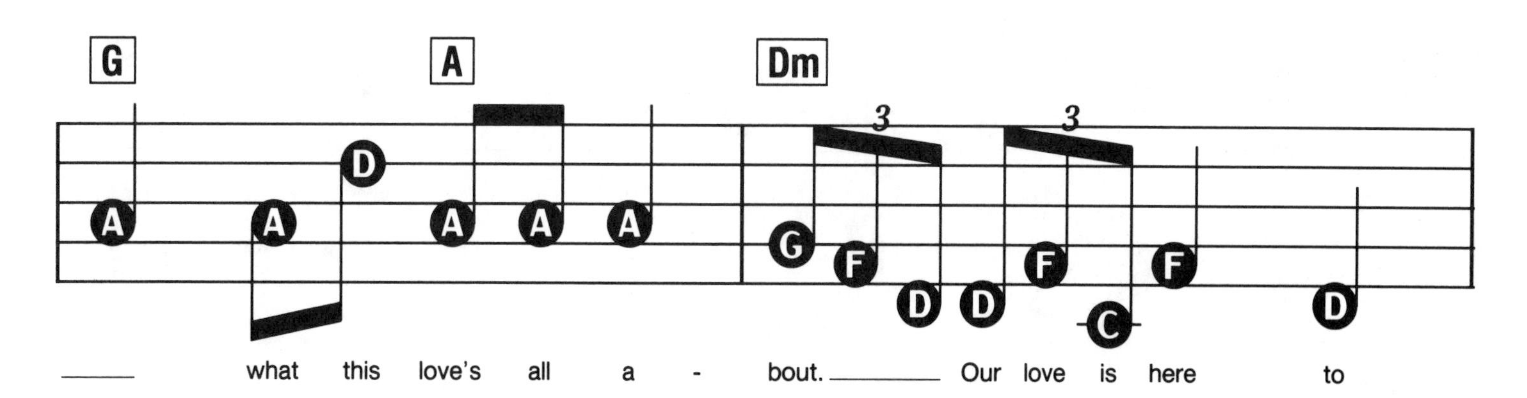
G
A
Dm
3
3
what this love's all a - bout. Our love is here to

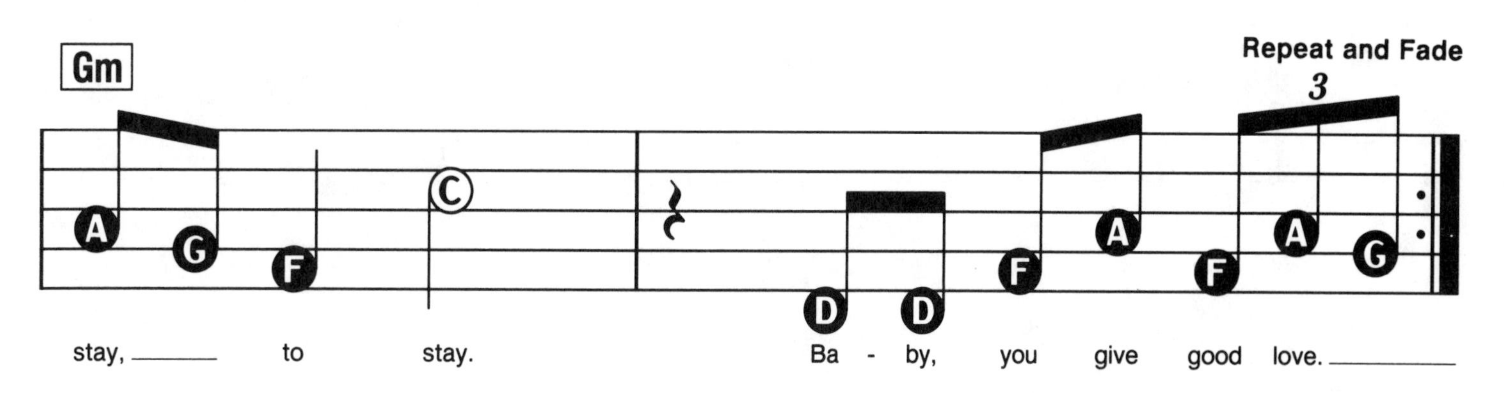
Gm
Repeat and Fade
3
stay, to stay. Ba - by, you give good love.

Your Song

Registration 3
Rhythm: Swing or Pops

Words and Music by Elton John
and Bernie Taupin

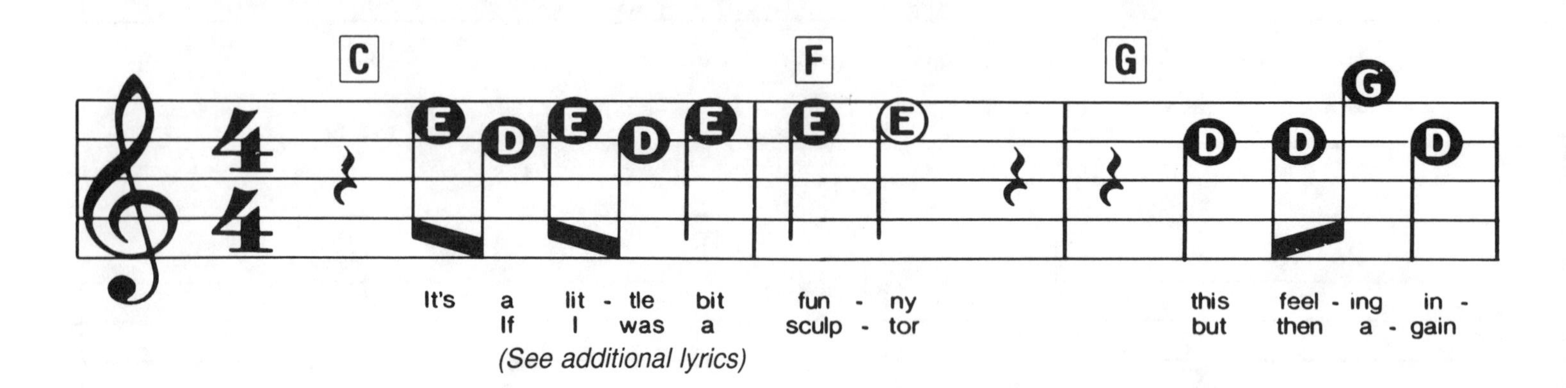

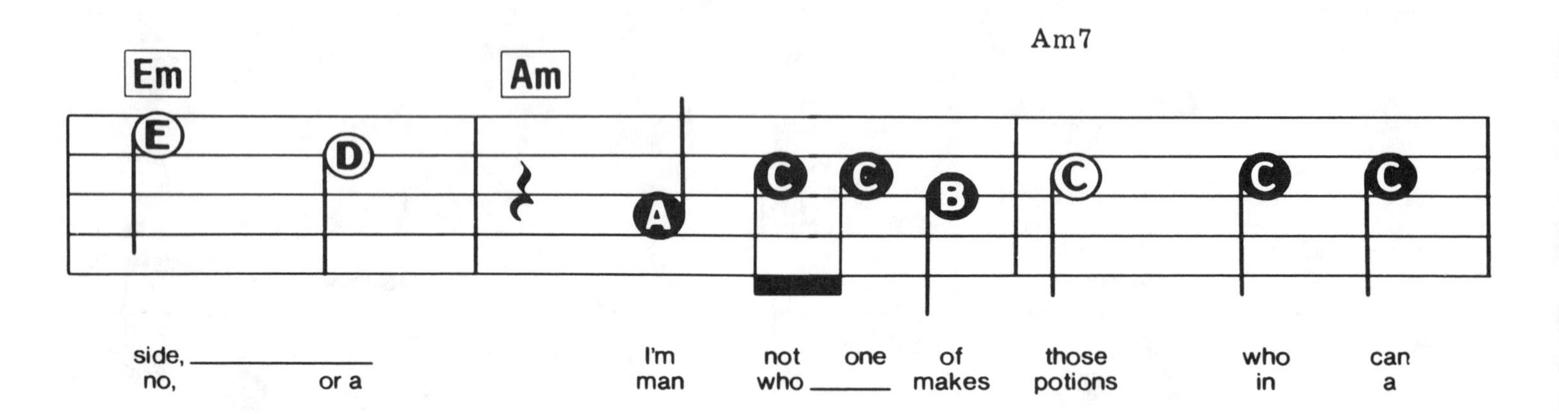

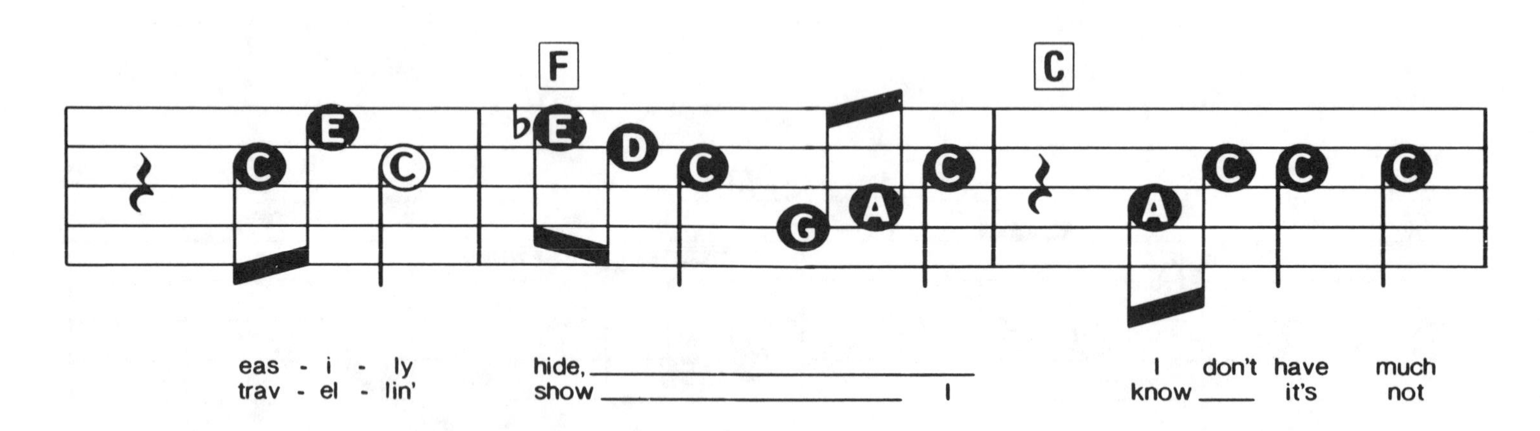

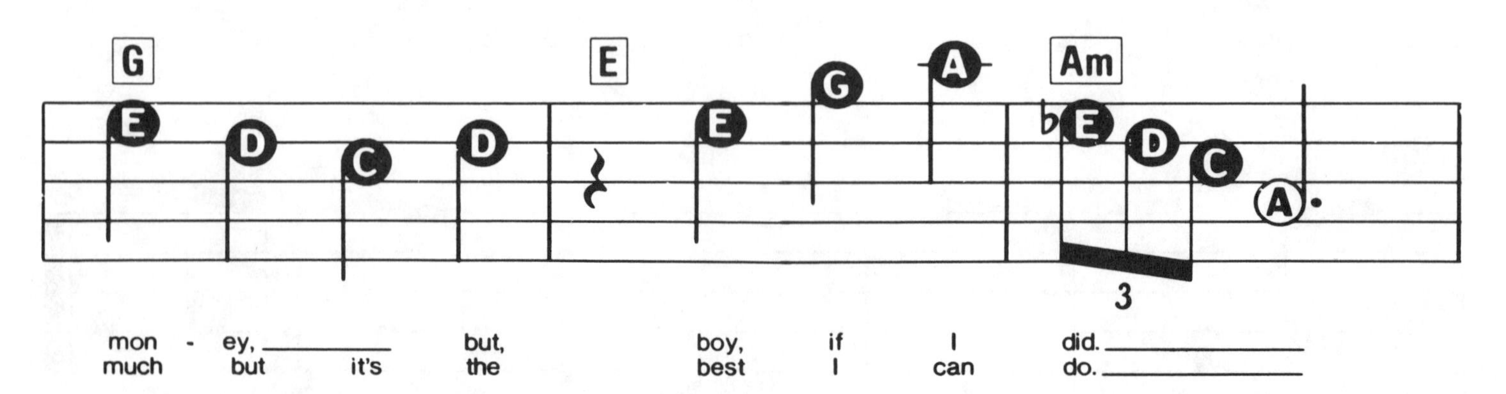

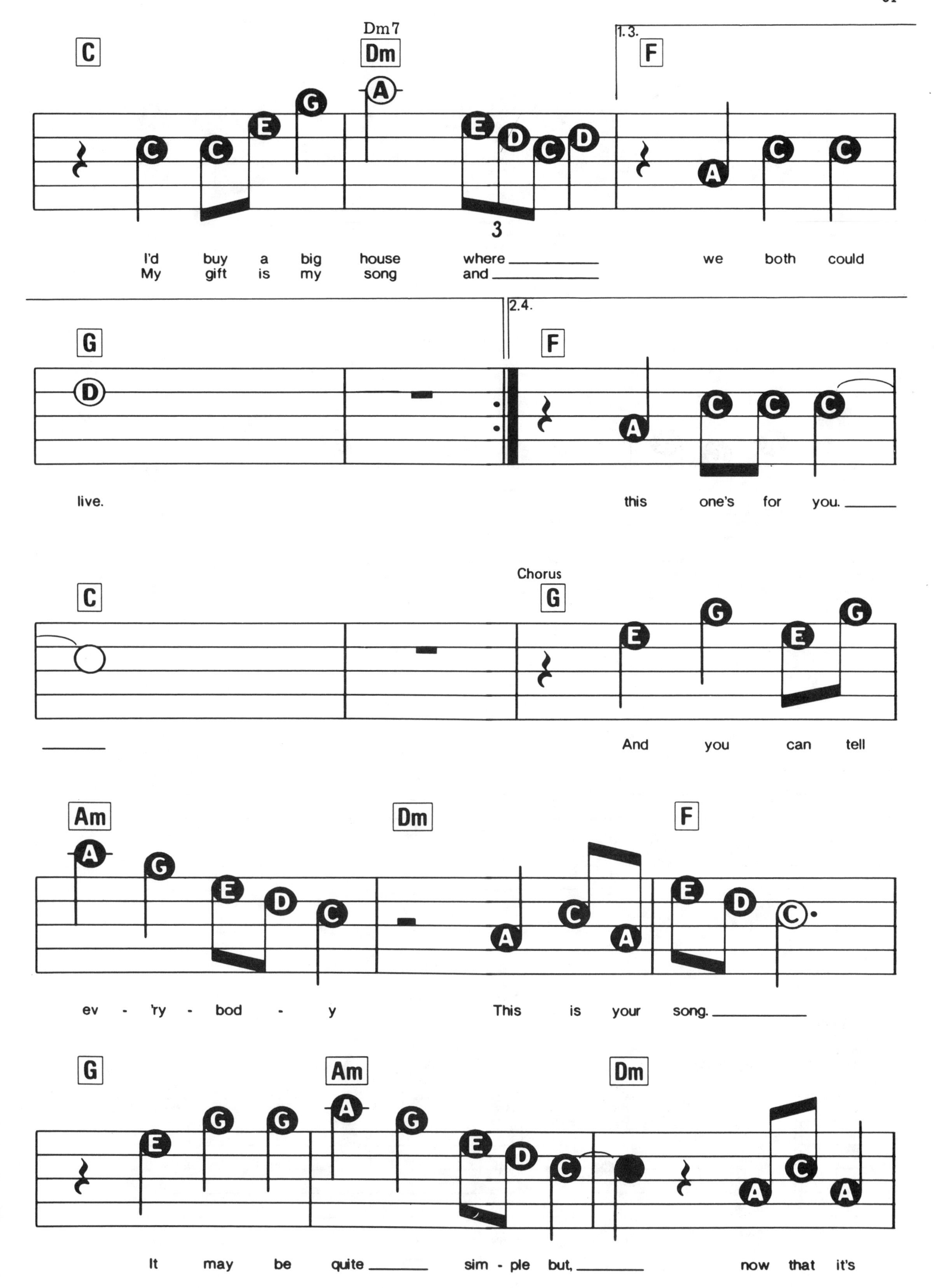
C
Dm7
Dm
1. 3.
F
I'd buy a big house where
My gift is my song and
we both could
G
2.4.
F
live.
this one's for you.
C
Chorus
G
And you can tell
Am
Dm
F
ev - 'ry - bod - y
This is your song.
G
Am
Dm
It may be quite
sim - ple but,
now that it's

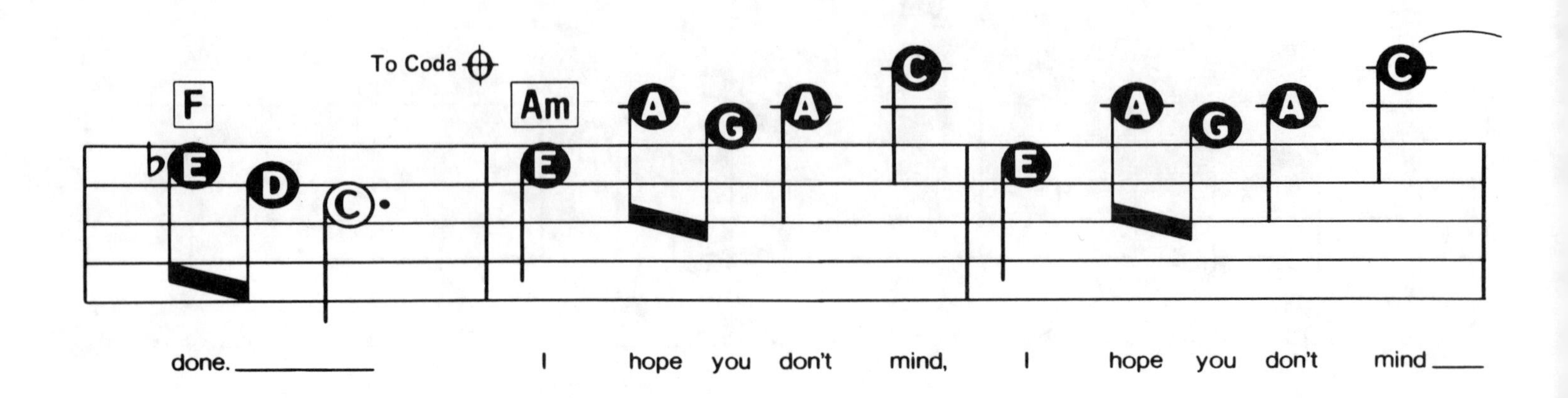
To Coda
F
Am
done.
I hope you don't mind, I hope you don't mind

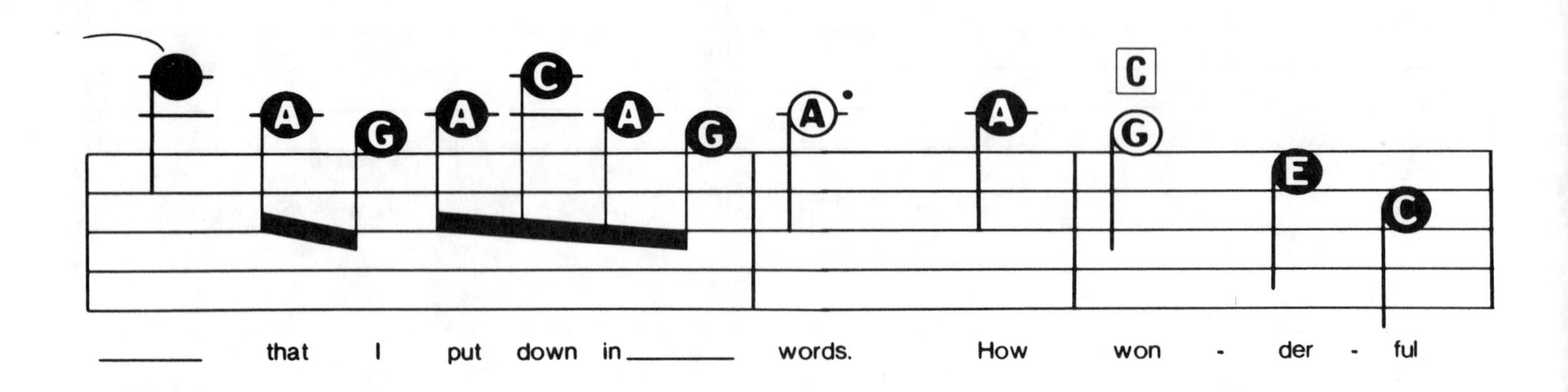
C
that I put down in words. How won - der - ful

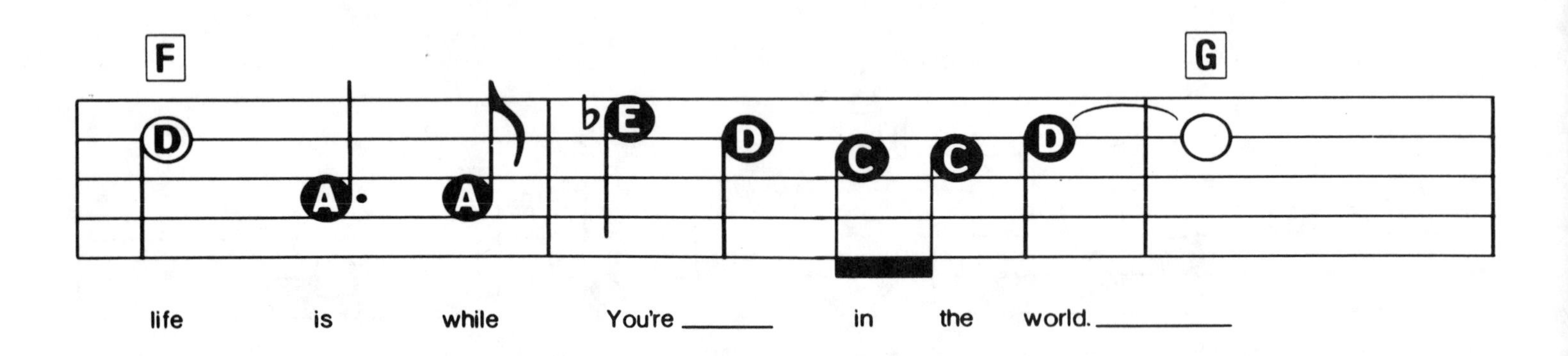
F
G
life is while You're in the world.

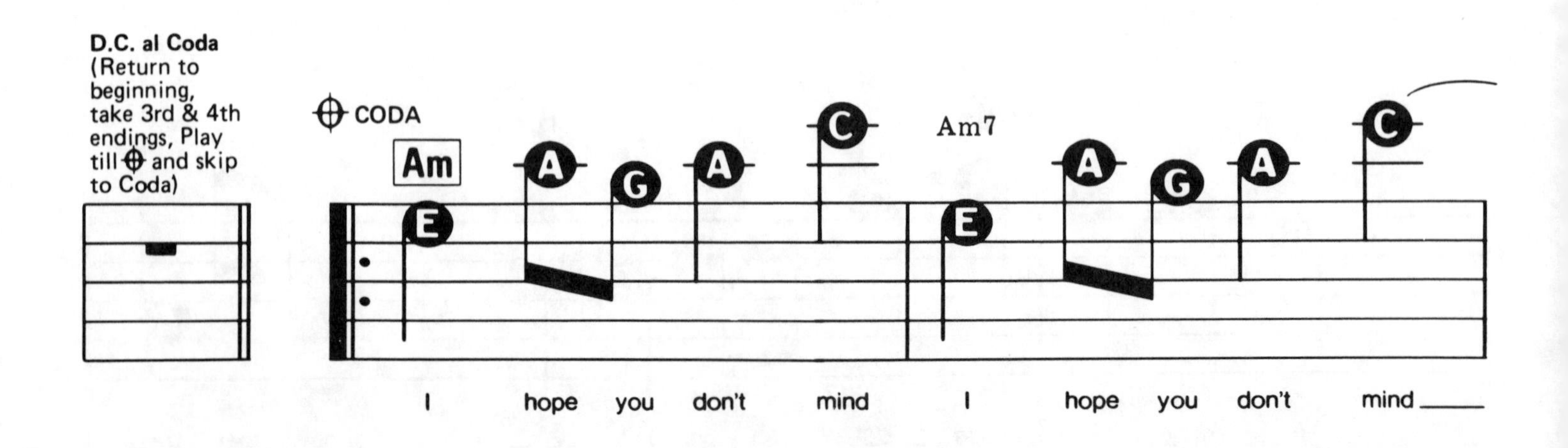
D.C. al Coda
(Return to beginning, take 3rd & 4th endings, Play till ⊕ and skip to Coda)
⊕ CODA
Am
Am7
I hope you don't mind I hope you don't mind

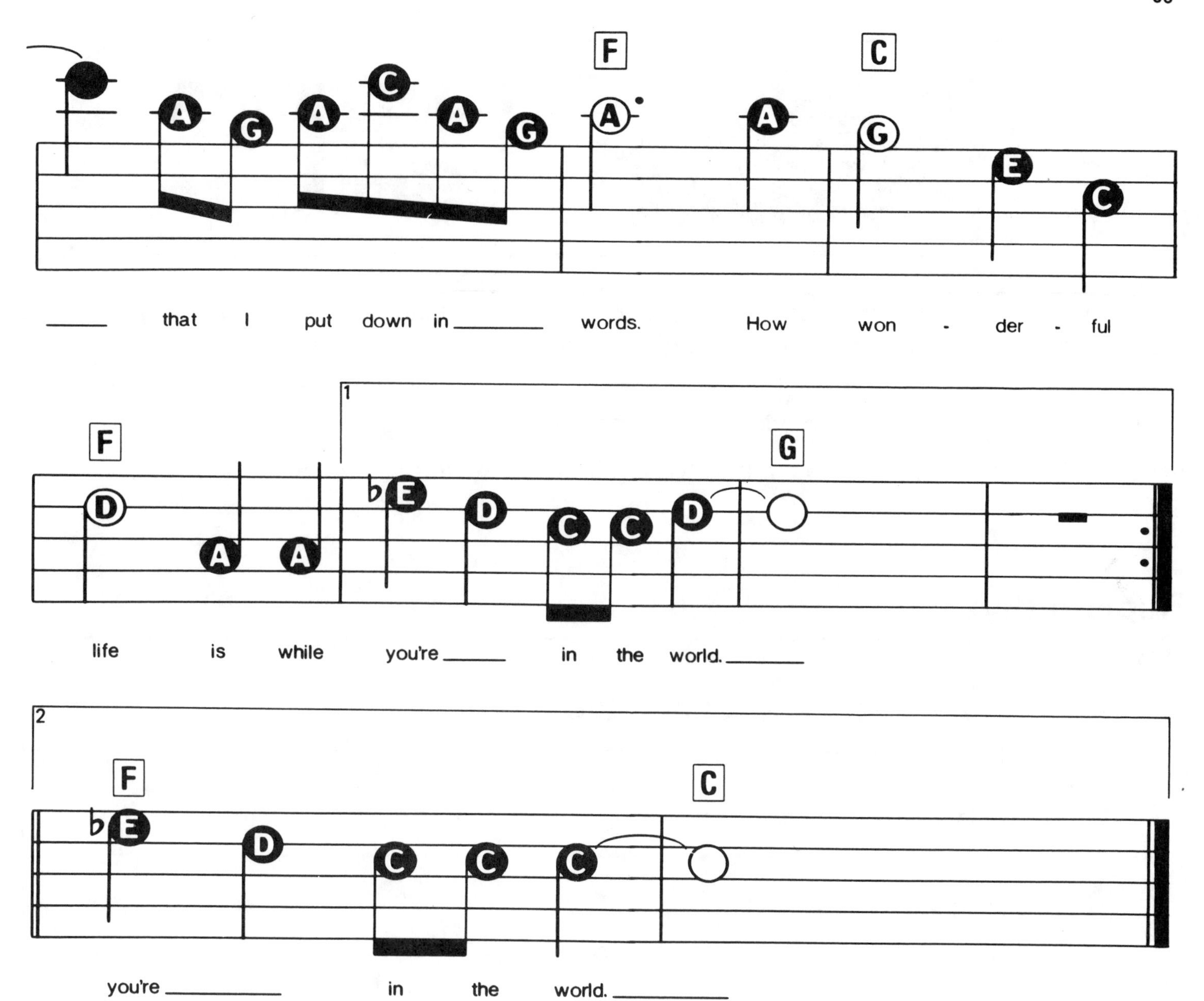

Additional Lyrics

3. I sat on the roof and kicked off the moss.
   well a few of the verses, well they've got me quite cross,
   But the sun's been quite kind while I wrote this song,
   It's for people like you that keep it turned on.

4. So excuse me forgetting but these things I do
   You see I've forgotten if they're green or they're blue,
   Anyway the thing is what I really mean
   Yours are the sweetest eyes I've ever seen.

Registration Guide

- Match the Registration number on the song to the corresponding numbered category below. Select and activate an instrumental sound available on your instrument.
- Choose an automatic rhythm appropriate to the mood and style of the song. (Consult your Owner's Guide for proper operation of automatic rhythm features.)
- Adjust the tempo and volume controls to comfortable settings.

Registration

1	Flute, Pan Flute, Jazz Flute
2	Clarinet, Organ
3	Violin, Strings
4	Brass, Trumpet
5	Synth Ensemble, Accordion, Brass
6	Pipe Organ, Harpsichord
7	Jazz Organ, Vibraphone, Vibes, Electric Piano, Jazz Guitar
8	Piano, Electric Piano
9	Trumpet, Trombone, Clarinet, Saxophone, Oboe
10	Violin, Cello, Strings